ALICE IN ORCHESTRALIA

*Preceded by her trumpeters and surrounded by her guard,
rode Titania, Queen of the Fairies*

A L I C E
IN ORCHESTRALIA

BY
ERNEST LA PRADE

FOREWORD BY
WALTER DAMROSCH

Illustrated by Carroll C. Snell

GARDEN CITY   NEW YORK
DOUBLEDAY & COMPANY, INC.
1949

TO
MY MOTHER

ACKNOWLEDGMENT

The author gratefully acknowledges his indebtedness to Miss Katharine Young, for many years identified with the New York Symphony Society's Concerts for Young People, at whose suggestion this little work was undertaken and whose aid and encouragement have been invaluable.

FOREWORD

"Alice in Orchestralia" is but another "Alice in Wonderland," for the author takes us in delightful fashion into the heart of that most wondrous land of all—the land of music.

Alice is to be envied, for there is hardly anything about a modern symphony orchestra—its make-up, its functions, its manner of speaking that universal language of human emotions—that she does not learn through the pages of this book. And it is all done in such a beguiling way that one might swear that it had been written by the whimsical and immortal author of the original "Alice in Wonderland."

I am glad that this work was written by an American, and am proud that he is also a member of my orchestra. I prophesy for this book a wide distribution wherever the English tongue is spoken and the love for music prevails.

Walter Damrosch.

CONTENTS

CHAPTER   PAGE

I.   THE BRASS TUNNEL   1

II.   A STRANGE JOURNEY   14

III. A TOPSY-TURVY REHEARSAL . .   24

IV. A QUARTET OUT OF TUNE . . .   39

V.   A TEA PARTY IN PANOPOLIS . .   57

VI. THE BRASSYDALE BAND . . .   75

VII. ALICE INSPECTS THE ARTILLERY .   99

VIII. A CONCERT IN ORCHESTRALIA . . 110

APPENDIX

THE ORCHESTRA 127

The Strings 128

The Wood-Wind 134

The Brasses 139

The Percussion Instruments . . . 142

THE ORCHESTRA AND ITS BUILDERS . . 147

TYPICAL PROGRAMS OF CONCERTS FOR CHILDREN AND CONCERTS FOR YOUNG PEOPLE 166

LIST OF ILLUSTRATIONS

Preceded by her trumpeters and surrounded by her guard, rode Titiana,
Queen of the Fairies . . . *Frontispiece*

FACING PAGE

"It's no use going there," he said . . 78

APPENDIX ILLUSTRATIONS

Usual Seating Plan in a Symphony
Orchestra 127

The Strings 129

The Wood-Wind 134

The Brasses 139

The Kettledrums 143

ALICE IN ORCHESTRALIA

CHAPTER I

THE BRASS TUNNEL

ALICE leaned over the railing of the box and gazed, fascinated, at the broad stage below her. It was filled with gentlemen all dressed exactly alike in tail coats and striped trousers, and seated in half-circles so that they all faced toward a little raised platform which stood at the center of the front edge of the stage. Round the platform was a brass railing, and behind the platform was a kind of desk made of beautifully carved wood. It was not the platform, however, nor the desk—nor even the gentlemen in tail coats—that interested Alice, but the strange-looking objects which the gentlemen held in their hands or between their knees, or which stood upon the floor beside them. These peculiar objects were of many different shapes and sizes, and there were so many of them that Alice was quite bewildered. Some were long and thin, some were short and fat, some seemed to be made of wood, some of silver, and some of brass, and each one seemed to be busily engaged in making a different kind of noise, for there rose from the stage a most extraordinary jumble of sounds. Alice was surprised, for she knew that the queer-looking objects were supposed to be musical instruments, and the sounds they were making did not sound at all like music.

"Perhaps," thought Alice, "they are having a sort of musical Caucus race—the kind of race in which everyone starts when he pleases, and runs in any direction he pleases, and leaves off when he pleases—and everybody wins a prize."

Alice, you should know, was not the same little girl who fell down the rabbit hole and had all those exciting adventures with the Dodo and the Duchess and other remarkable people, but she had read all about that other Alice and was rather proud that she had the same name as the little girl in the story. She was sure that they must be distantly related—third or fourth cousins, perhaps—and she wished that she too might fall down a rabbit hole or get through a looking-glass into Wonderland. Indeed, she was confident that some day she would find her way into that delightful country, so she kept her eyes open for likely-looking mirrors and rabbit holes, and was ready to follow the very first white rabbit she saw with a watch and a waistcoat.

To-day Alice's mother had brought her to hear her first symphony concert, and she was very much excited about it. She was fond of music and took the greatest interest in her piano lessons—she practised an hour every day—but she had never seen or heard a symphony orchestra until this moment. The number and variety of the instruments astonished her, and she wondered whether they could possibly all play at once without getting mixed up. She wished she knew the names of all of them, and how they were played, and what sort of sound each one made. Her seat was almost directly over the right-hand side of the stage, so that she could see them all quite plainly, and she began to try to pick out the ones that she *did* know.

"There," she said to herself, "are the violins." (She recognized them because her brother

Hugh had a violin on which he had recently begun to take lessons.)   "But what a lot of them there are! Dozens and dozens! Why, they reach right across the stage in a double row— and there are lots more behind them. And those big things at the back that look like giant violins are the bass viols—I know that. Oh! and there's a trombone—and another—and another. Three of them! I know them by the way they slide in and out. They look as if they went right down the men's throats. I wonder if they do. Now, let me see, are there any more that I know?" She looked carefully at all the instruments, but there were no others whose names she was sure of. One she thought might be a flute, and there were several, of different shapes and sizes, which she supposed were horns; but she was not at all certain.

One enormous instrument particularly fascinated Alice. It was made of gleaming brass and looked like a huge snake all coiled up with its mouth wide open. It was almost underneath the box in which Alice sat, and for a moment she had the unpleasant feeling that it had opened its great mouth in order to swallow her, as a boa constrictor swallows a sheep. She soon realized however, that such a notion was absurd.

"Of course it isn't *really* a boa constrictor," she told herself, "because it's made of brass—and besides, its mouth is really more like a funnel. It certainly looks big enough to swallow me; but if it did," she went on, smiling at the idea, "it would most likely choke to death, because its throat gets smaller and smaller all the way down to its tail. Now, I wonder where its throat ends and its tail begins?"

That was an extremely difficult question to answer, and Alice was still pondering over it when her speculations were interrupted by a loud clapping of hands. Looking up she saw a very elegantly dressed gentleman, also in a tail coat and striped trousers, who had just come through a door at the back of the stage. Making his way to the little platform with the brass railing, he mounted upon it and smiled and bowed to the audience. Then, turning round toward the orchestra, he rapped upon the desk with a little white stick, waited until everybody was quite still, and then gave the signal to the orchestra to begin to play.

Glancing at her programme, Alice was delighted to find that the first number was Mendelssohn's Overture to "A Midsummer Night's Dream."

"Oh, how jolly!" she exclaimed to herself. "I wonder if there will be anything in it about Bottom and Puck and the other fairies!" For Alice was well acquainted with the charming people of Shakespeare's fairy play. She had not only read about them in Lamb's "Tales from Shakespeare," but she had also seen the play performed, only the summer before, by a company of actors who had visited her school. So she leaned over the railing and listened very attentively.

At the first sound of the mysterious magic chords with which the overture begins, a spell seemed to fall upon the vast auditorium. The stage was changed, as if by a wave of Titania's fairy wand, into a lovely forest glade surrounded by giant oaks and flooded with silvery moonlight. For a moment all was still; not a leaf rustled, not a cricket chirped. Then, suddenly, came a sound of pattering feet, tinkling elfin laughter, and faintly, in the distance, a fanfare of tiny trumpets. Titania and her court were approaching. Nearer and nearer they came, until finally, with a lively fanfare from the fairy trumpets, the procession appeared in the moonlight and marched gaily round the glade. Preceded by her trumpeters and surrounded by her guard, who were armed with lances of sharpest spike-rush, rode Titania, Queen of the Fairies. Her chariot was a moon-flower drawn by six spirited fireflies; on her brow sparkled a diadem of tiny stars, and in her hand she held a shining wand.

With great pomp and ceremony the procession circled the glade and drew up at one side, and instantly a company of elfin dancers appeared before it and began to perform an entrancing ballet. Round and round they twirled, now in couples, now in groups, now joining hands in one great circle which revolved so swiftly that it made one dizzy to watch it. Again they would leap into the air and go whirling madly about among the tree-tops, their little wings humming like bumblebees and their laughter tinkling like silver bells.

All at once they were gone, and for a little while the glade was empty. Then from the depths of the forest came a loud and harsh "Heehaw!" and into the moonlight strode a most extraordinary creature. It had the body of a man, dressed in a leather jacket and short breeches, but its head was the grave and solemn head of an ass. Alice recognized him at once: he was Bottom the weaver. He walked up and down the glade in a very pompous manner and attempted to sing a song, but he must have had a very bad cold in his head, for his voice was dreadfully hoarse and gruff.

When he had finished his song Bottom lay down upon a grassy bank and fell fast asleep, and he had hardly begun to snore when a very lively little elf all dressed in red came leaping and somersaulting down the glade, snatched off the ass's head and darted away into the forest, leaving Bottom's own head in its proper place on his shoulders. Then all Bottom's friends—Peter Quince the carpenter, Snout the tinker, Starveling, Snug, and Flute—came out of the wood and wakened Bottom, and the whole company joined in a jolly and extremely comical dance. They danced themselves away at last, and then back came all the fairies—Queen Titania with King Oberon, followed by Puck and Peaseblossom and Mustardseed and all the rest —tripping, dancing, singing, and laughing as merrily as before

But soon the first faint blush of dawn appeared. The night was nearly over, and, as no well-brought-up fairy ever stays out after daybreak, away they flitted to their homes in acorn cups and rosebuds, to sleep until the stars should wake again. And as they vanished the enchanted glade slowly faded away, the trees changed back into bass viols and the grassy banks into gentlemen in tail coats. The spell was ended.

Everybody applauded heartily. The conductor bowed with great dignity and went away through the door at the back of the stage; but as the applause continued he came back again and bowed once more and waved his hand at the orchestra, and all the gentlemen in tail coats stood up and looked very solemn. Alice did not applaud. She sat quite still and stared hard at the stage, hoping that the fairies would reappear; but it was no use—they refused to show themselves again. Presently Alice's mother leaned forward and said:

"How did you like it, dear?"

Alice turned round, her eyes bright with excitement. "Oh, Mother!" she exclaimed, "wasn't it wonderful! I saw Puck and Titania and Bottom and—and all, just as plain as could be!"

"Did you really?" said her mother. "Why, it must have been almost as good as seeing the play."

"It was better," Alice declared, emphatically,

"lots better; because in the play the fairies were just grown-up people dressed like fairies, and these were real ones—little tiny ones, like the fairies in story books, with hats made out of buttercups and frocks made out of daffodils. Puck had wings exactly like a dragon fly's."

"How charming he must have looked!" said her mother.

"Didn't you see him too?" Alice inquired.

Her mother shook her head. "I'm afraid my eyes are not so sharp as yours," she said. "But I heard him quite clearly."

Alice was disappointed. It seemed to her that anyone should have been able to see the fairies—they were so plainly visible to her. But she said nothing more about it, and presently became interested again in looking at the various instruments of the orchestra. The one which looked like a brass boa constrictor still reared its enormous funnel-shaped mouth almost underneath Alice's seat. It seemed to yawn invitingly, as much as to say: "Won't you drop in for a moment? There's plenty of room—I'm sure you'd find it very comfortable and cozy."

"That's all very well," Alice thought, "but how should I get out again? Of course, if I were like the Alice in the story I could eat a little cake or a bit of mushroom or something and grow smaller and smaller until I was small enough to crawl right through and out at the end of its tail. That would be fun. I wouldn't be any bigger than a fairy when I got out. I wonder if the fairies would let me come and dance with them? They might think I was a fairy too—only I shouldn't have any wings. I wonder if there are any fairies without wings. Of course, I might borrow some from a bumble-bee or a butterfly or a moth. I think I should like a moth's wings best—they're so soft and downy."

It was a delightful idea, and Alice would very likely have gone on thinking about it until, in her imagination, she had got herself fitted out with a pair of wings of the most fashionable design, been crowned queen of the fairies, and had a row with Oberon into the bargain; but just then the conductor reappeared and prepared to begin the next number.

Looking again at her programme Alice learned that the next number was a "Symphony in C," by Schubert; but as she did not know what a "symphony" was she was little wiser than before. It proved, however, to be very agreeable to listen to. Its lovely melodies and warm, rich harmonies seemed to caress and lull Alice into a state of delicious dreaminess, and leaning back in her chair she closed her eyes in order to enjoy more fully this delightful sensation. She felt as if she were sitting in a swing which swayed gently to and fro in the shade of a spreading oak tree, while a gentle summer breeze fanned her cheeks and softly tousled her hair. The air was warm and drowsy, full of the scent of new-mown hay and the hum of bees, and Alice thought she would like to sit there with her eyes closed and dream daydreams for hours and hours. So she was rather annoyed when she heard a voice calling her name.

"Oh, dear!" she said to herself, "just when I was feeling so nice and comfy! Now I wonder who it can be that wants me."

The voice was very faint and far away, so Alice sat quite still with her eyes closed, thinking that she might have been mistaken. She was not mistaken, however, for soon she heard the voice again, faintly but quite distinctly, calling, "Alice! Alice!" So with a sigh she opened her eyes and sat up—and then she opened her mouth as well, and stared, and rubbed her eyes, and stared again; for what she saw was most surprising. Just in front of her was a high green hill, in the side of which was a circular opening like the entrance to a tunnel. Evidently it was a very long tunnel, for though Alice was looking directly into it she could not see the other end; and what seemed still more remarkable was that it appeared to be made entirely of polished brass. Alice was wondering how many barrels of brass polish it took to keep the tunnel so bright and shiny, and thinking that she shouldn't particularly care to have the job of polishing it every week, when she became aware that the voice was still calling her name, and that the sound undoubtedly came from inside the tunnel.

"Well," she said, aloud, "I'm sure I don't know who they are or what they want, but I s'pose I'd better go and find out." So she jumped out of the swing and went skipping down the long brass tunnel.

CHAPTER II

A STRANGE JOURNEY

ON AND on went Alice, sometimes walking, sometimes skipping merrily as she hummed a tune to herself. There was nothing at all to see in the tunnel, and after a time she began to think that she must have come a very long way. However, she seemed no nearer the end of the tunnel than when she had started: and when she looked behind her, expecting to see the round spot of daylight at the entrance, it had disappeared.

"Well," she said, surprised, "that's queer. I must have come round a bend without noticing it. This is certainly the longest tunnel I ever

heard of, but there *must* be an end to it somewhere, so I may as well keep on walking," and
on she went once more, humming her cheerful
little tune.

The curved brass walls of the tunnel gleamed
and shone so brightly that presently it occurred
to Alice to wonder where the light came from
which was reflected with such brilliance by the
polished metal. She saw no electric bulbs or
gas jets, and she couldn't understand why the
tunnel was not quite dark inside, like those she
had passed through on railroad trains.

"I s'pose," she decided, after puzzling over
the question for some time—"I s'pose that one
day some sunbeams must have wandered in here
by mistake, and then they got lost and couldn't
find the way out. Oh, dear! What if *I* should
get lost and never find *my* way out?"

She felt just a wee bit frightened and had begun to walk faster when, all at once, she turned
a sharp bend and came to the end of the tunnel.
But instead of coming out into the open air, as
she had expected, she found herself in a long
hall with a vaulted roof, at either end of which
was the entrance to another tunnel like the one
through which she had come. The floor of the
hall was level, but down the middle of it was a

wide gap about four feet deep with two shiny rails running along the bottom. Alice concluded that she must be in a railway station—although she had never before seen a railway station made entirely of brass—and she had hardly come to that conclusion when a train, also made entirely of brass, without a locomotive, slid noiselessly out of one of the tunnels and came to a stop. Instantly all the doors opened, apparently of their own accord, and a faint, muffled voice which seemed to come from everywhere at once said, "All aboard—watch-a-door!"

Without stopping to think that she hadn't the least idea where it would take her, Alice got into one of the cars, the doors closed, and away went the train down the tunnel. Alice sat down and looked about her. Except for herself the car she was in was quite empty, and as far as she could see she was the only person in the entire train. She had never heard of a train without any passengers or even a conductor. "But," she thought, "maybe it's a good thing there isn't any conductor, since I haven't got a ticket. He might put me off the train—and I'm sure I'm tired enough of walking."

Just then, the queer, muffled voice which she

had heard as she got into the train called out something that sounded like "Neckstar oofty ooftree!" The voice sounded so near that Alice jumped. She looked all about her but could see no one, and she was beginning to feel a bit uneasy when the train stopped at another station, the doors all opened as before, and the voice said again, "All aboard—watch-a-door!" This time Alice was ready for it, and discovered that it came from a sort of tin trumpet over her head. She decided that it must be some kind of talking machine, and wondered how it knew what to say and when to say it. Meanwhile the train had started again, and after a few moments the voice in the trumpet spoke again: "Neckstar oofty ooftree!"

"It's rather hard to understand," thought Alice. "I s'pose 'neckstar' means 'next stop,' and the rest of it must be the name of the station —something street, very likely. How anybody can tell which station is which I'm sure I don't know, because all the names sound exactly alike. But the stations all look exactly alike too, so p'raps it doesn't make much difference which one you get out at."

On went the train, through mile after mile of shining brass tunnel, stopping now and then at stations whose names all sounded like "oofty ooftree." As nobody ever got either into the train or out of it, and as nothing exciting had happened for a long while, Alice began to grow restless. She had nearly made up her mind to get out, herself, at the next station, when suddenly the train shot out of the tunnel into dazzling sunlight. Alice looked eagerly out of the window and saw that she was travelling through a very beautiful country. On either side of the railway spread lovely green meadows full of daisies and buttercups, while in the distance were rolling hills covered with trees. Here and there she saw a tiny house, painted white, with green blinds and a red roof, and all overgrown with ivy.

"Last stop—All out!" said the voice in the trumpet, quite distinctly this time. Alice obediently stepped out upon the station platform, and she had no sooner done so than the doors closed again and the train dashed off in the direction from which it had come.

Alice looked all about her, hoping to see somebody to whom she might speak, for there were a great many questions she wanted to ask. But there was not a living creature in sight; the station was as deserted as the train had been.

"Well," thought Alice, "this is certainly the loneliest place I ever saw. But maybe it's Sunday, and everybody's at church—or p'r'aps this is one of those countries where all the people take naps after luncheon. Anyhow, I may as well walk about a bit and see what the village is like; and I *might* meet somebody to talk to." There was a door near the center of the platform which looked as if it might lead to the street, and Alice had just started toward it when she was startled by a loud rumbling sound close beside her. The only object on the station platform was a curiously shaped trunk which looked somewhat like an enormous bottle with a long neck, only it was square instead of round. It stood on end with its back against the wall, and it was rather more than twice as tall as Alice. She examined the trunk with curiosity, wondering what on earth could be inside it, and whether the sound she had heard could possibly have proceeded from it. The sound was repeated, louder, deeper, more rumbling than before. There could be no doubt about it: it *did* come from the trunk. And, stranger even than that, it sounded remarkably like a snore. In fact, it was a snore—an immense, ear-filling, ground-shaking giant of a snore, but unmistakably a snore. It grew gradually louder, rising and falling in regular waves of sound, and then suddenly it broke off with a choke and a snort, and was followed by a violent pounding on the inside of the trunk. Then an incredibly deep bass voice shouted angrily, "Let me out! Open the door, I say, and let me out!"

At first, Alice was too much astonished to move, but as the pounding and shouting continued she collected her wits and decided that something must be done. The trunk, she saw, was fortunately not locked, but the lid was held down by two clasps, one near the bottom and the other near the top. The bottom clasp she undid without difficulty, but the upper one was quite out of her reach; however, by climbing upon a bench, she managed to reach the upper clasp and unfasten it. As she did so the lid of the trunk flew open and out lurched a huge corpulent and evidently indignant bass viol.

Alice almost fell off the bench in her astonishment, for never before had she seen, or even heard of, a bass viol such as this one. It had legs and arms and a mouth and two very prominent eyes, all of which it proceeded at once to exercise, very much to Alice's alarm. Stalking up to her it glared at her with its round, staring eyes, brandished its fist under her nose and roared at her like an angry bull.

"Now, then!" it bellowed, "what do you mean by it, eh? Shutting me up in there and nearly smothering me to death! What do you mean by it?—that's what I should like to know!"

"Excuse me," Alice stammered, frightened, "I—I didn't shut you up; I only—I let you out. You see," she explained, "I only came by the last train, and I didn't know you were in there until I heard you sno—I mean, shouting."

The Bass Viol stopped brandishing its fist and regarded her suspiciously. Then it said, apparently somewhat mollified: "Well, I suppose it was those naughty Ukulele boys—they're always up to mischief. Just wait till I catch them!" Then it added gruffly: "I'm much obliged to you, I'm sure."

"You're quite welcome," said Alice, politely. The Bass Viol's manner was so much less menacing that she was no longer frightened, and her curiosity promptly got the better of her.

"Excuse me," she said, "but would you mind telling me how you came to be in that trunk?"

"It's not a trunk," growled the Bass Viol; "it's a bed—a new one, just sent from the factory. I got in it to see if it fitted, and it was so comfortable that I must have dozed off for a moment. And then I suppose those kids came along and shut me in. Just wait till I lay my hands on 'em—they're a disgrace to the town! I don't see why they're allowed to live in a place like Fiddladelphia."

"Oh!" said Alice, "is this Philadelphia? Why, I've been here before. But somehow it doesn't look quite the same——"

"I said Fiddladelphia, not Philadelphia," the Bass Viol interrupted. "It's *not* the same at all. Philadelphia is in Pennsylvania, unless I've forgotten my geography, and Fiddladelphia is the capital of Orchestralia."

"I see," said Alice, rather doubtfully. "I'm afraid I don't remember *my* geography very well. I *think* I've heard of Orchestralia—it sounds familiar—but I'm not quite sure. Is it a new country that's just been discovered?"

"No and yes," replied the Bass Viol. "That is, it's *not* a new country—in fact, it's a very old one—but *you've* just discovered it; and there are millions of people who have not discovered it yet, though it's much more widely known to-day than it was a few years ago. By the way, how did you say you got here?"

"I came in a funny sort of train that ran most

of the way in a brass tunnel," said Alice. "I think it must have been the Tube."

"You mean the Tuba," the Bass Viol corrected her. "That's the way most of them come."

"Are there any more people here?" Alice inquired. "I mean—regular people—like me?"

"Oh, very likely," replied the Bass Viol. "You're the first one I've seen to-day, but we have quite a lot of visitors nowadays. I suppose you'd like to look around a bit now that you're here?"

"Oh, I should love to!" Alice exclaimed; "only I'm afraid I might lose my way."

"That's all right," said the Bass Viol, reassuringly. "I'll show you around myself. Come along, we'd better not waste any time."

Its ill-temper had quite disappeared, and it beamed upon Alice with such fatherly benevolence that she did not hesitate to take the hand it held out to her as it led the way out of the station and into the village of Fiddladelphia.

CHAPTER III

A TOPSY–TURVY REHEARSAL

LICE and the Bass Viol emerged from the station and started across a beautiful little park full of shrubbery and of ornamental flower beds laid out in the form of graceful musical signs. There were staves and clefs and various kinds of notes, and in the center of the park on a little knoll was an entire piece of music composed of growing flowers of different colors. Alice was staring at it and wondering what the tune might be, when the Bass Viol said, as if reading her thoughts:

"I wonder if you recognize the tune?"

"I'm afraid I don't," Alice admitted, "though there's something familiar about it. I'm not very good at reading music; but I could play it on the piano," she added confidently.

"What a funny idea!" exclaimed the Bass Viol. "You might just as well say that you couldn't read print but that you could play it on the typewriter. I shouldn't call that being able to read, would you?"

"Why, n—no," said Alice, "I s'pose not."

"Well, music is like print—either you can read it or you can't. Now, I'm sure you can read that piece of music if you try. Come, I'll give you the first note: *Do*"—he sang the tone in what was for him a high falsetto voice. "Now, what's the next one?"

"*Re*," sang Alice promptly.

"Right; and the next?"

"*Mi.*"

"Right again. Now go ahead and sing the whole tune. You'll find it's not at all difficult once you know how to go about it."

Thus encouraged, Alice began, and was surprised at the ease with which she sang the piece through from the beginning to end.

"Not bad," said the Bass Viol when she had

finished. "You have a very good ear, and not a bad tone for a wind instrument."

"Why, the very idea!" Alice protested. "I'm not a wind instrument."

"Oh, aren't you?" said the Bass Viol, rather sarcastically. "Then what kind of an instrument do you call yourself? You certainly aren't a stringed instrument."

"I'm not an instrument at all," Alice declared indignantly. "I'm a—I'm a human being."

"You may be whatever you like in your own country," said the Bass Viol, "but here you're an instrument. Everybody is."

Alice was silent for a moment. She was a little offended. Then an idea occurred to her and her face brightened.

"Is *that* why they call this country Orchestralia?" she asked.

"Naturally; because all the instruments of the orchestra live here."

"Oh, goody!" cried Alice. "And can I see them all, and will you tell me their names and all about them?"

"I will introduce you to them—then you can ask them all the questions you like about themselves."

"I hope they won't mind," said Alice, "there

are so many things I want to know. Do you mind answering questions?"

"Not at all," said the Bass Viol, once more in a good humor. "You may ask me as many as you please."

"Then I may as well begin now," said Alice, "because there are going to be lots and lots of them. First of all, can all the instruments that live here walk and talk just as you can?"

"Yes, indeed," the Bass Viol assured her.

"Then why don't they do it in—in my country?"

"Well, you see, it isn't necessary. In your country there is always somebody to carry us about, and plenty of people like yourself to do the talking. So we just let you do the walking and the talking for us while we make music for you. That's fair, isn't it?"

Alice admitted that it seemed so. By this time they had left the park and were walking down a shady winding road between rows of little houses set in the middle of delightful gardens. Some of the houses were of red brick, some of soft gray stone, some of cream-colored plaster with dark oak beams; some had red roofs, some green, and some had roofs in which many colors were blended in a rich pattern like that of a Persian rug.   Most of the houses were covered with vines and creepers which seemed almost to be part of them.

"Pretty, isn't it?" remarked the Bass Viol, waving its hand toward the houses and gardens.

"I never saw anything so lovely!" said Alice. "It's all so—so restful! Everything seems to match."

"That's just it—it's harmonious. Harmony is our motto here. That's why it's such a pleasant country to live in."

"Is it always as quiet as this?" Alice inquired. "I haven't seen anybody yet but you. Where are all the other people—I mean instruments?"

"Oh," said the Bass Viol, "they're all at the rehearsal. We're on our way there now, so you'll soon see them—all the fiddles, that is; the others don't live in Fiddladelphia, except a few of the lower-class stringed instruments, such as the guitars and mandolins and those pesky ukuleles, who hang about the outskirts of the village. By rights they ought not to be here at all; they're not members of the orchestra. But it seems impossible to keep out the undesirable element, even in Orchestralia."

Alice couldn't help thinking that her amiable

guide must be just a wee bit snobbish, and she wondered if life in this extraordinary country was, after all, as perfectly harmonious as the Bass Viol had claimed. However, she said nothing about it, and presently her thoughts went racing off on another tack.

"You said," she reminded the Bass Viol, "that only fiddles lived in Fiddladelphia; but you're not a fiddle, are you?"

"Of course I'm a fiddle," it declared, proudly.

"But," Alice persisted, "I thought 'fiddle' was only another name for a violin."

"Not at all," said the Bass Viol. " 'Fiddle' means a stringed instrument played with a bow. We all belong to the fiddle, or viol, family. The violin is merely one member of it—and the smallest one, at that. But here we are at the Conservatory, where we hold our rehearsals. Now you shall see all my brothers and nephews and cousins."

They had arrived at a very large and beautiful building all of white stone, with a row of tall columns across the front. Mounting a flight of broad stone steps they passed through a magnificent marble entrance hall and into a large auditorium. On the stage a small group of instruments were assembled, and many others sat about in different parts of the hall, but there were plenty of vacant seats.

"Let us go right down to the front," said the Bass Viol, "so that you can see plainly. We can hear perfectly in any part of the hall—the acoustics are so good."

"Acoustics?" said Alice. "What are they?"

"Why, acoustics are—ahem!—acoustics, you see—— Well, it's rather difficult to explain, but they're the things that make music or speaking sound well in a hall."

"What do they look like?" Alice inquired. The name suggested something with horns and four legs, but she saw nothing of that description in the auditorium.

"Oh, you can't see them. They're only spaces and proportions and—and all that sort of thing," the Bass Viol explained, rather lamely. "As a matter of fact, nobody knows exactly what they are; but if music sounds well in a place you say that place has good acoustics, and if it doesn't sound well you say the place has bad acoustics. Does that make it clear?"

Alice thought it was still rather confusing, but as it didn't seem to be so *very* important she merely nodded her head and dismissed the matter from her mind.

By this time they had reached the front of the auditorium and taken seats near the center of the stage, from which point Alice could see the performers quite plainly. There were four of them: three small fiddles and one which was about half the size of Alice's friend, the Bass Viol. They seemed to be having a consultation about the music they were going to play, but in a moment they all went to the rear of the stage where a row of tall, narrow cupboards stood against the wall. Each fiddle opened a cupboard and took from it what appeared to be a man dressed in a tail coat and striped trousers.

"Look! Look!" cried Alice, excitedly. "They keep human beings shut up in those little closets!"

"They're not human beings," the Bass Viol corrected her, "they're only musicians."

"Only musicians?" said Alice, puzzled. "Aren't musicians human beings?"

"Well, at any rate, these are not," said the Bass Viol. "They're only mechanical dummies that we use for making music."

"Can't you make music without them?" Alice asked.

"Certainly not," said the Bass Viol. "In your country a fiddler can't make music without a fiddle to play on, can he? Well, we can't make music without a fiddler to play on us. So we all have our fiddlers, just as your fiddlers all have their fiddles; and we keep them in boxes, just as your violinists keep their instruments."

"Well," said Alice, "I s'pose that's fair; but somehow it seems all topsy-turvy."

"You'll soon get used to the idea," said the Bass Viol, reassuringly. "Things always seem more or less topsy-turvy when you first visit a strange land."

Having led their mechanical players to the front of the stage and seated them so that they faced each other, two on the left and two on the right, the fiddles then placed their bows in the players' right hands and their necks in the players' left hands. At a word from one of the small fiddles, who seemed to be the leader, they all sprang to their positions—the small fiddles underneath their players' chins, the large fiddle between its player's knees—and the automatic musicians promptly began to play.

"These four instruments constitute what is called a string quartet," said the Bass Viol, speaking in a whisper in order not to disturb anybody. "I suppose you know them all?"

"Why," said Alice, also in a whisper, "I don't

know the big one's name, but the three small ones are violins."

"Wrong," said the Bass Viol; "only two of them are violins—those in front. The one back there at the left is a viola. He's an older brother of the violins and looks very much like them for he's the same shape and has four strings, just as they have; but if you look more closely you'll see that he's a little larger, and if you listen very carefully you'll hear that his voice is a little deeper and has rather a sad quality. The big fellow facing the viola is a violoncello, but all his friends call him 'Cello for short."

"I suppose," said Alice, "that 'violincello' means a big violin."

"Wrong again," the Bass Viol corrected her; "it's 'violoncello,' not 'violincello.' Now let's get these names all straight in our minds: 'viola' is Italian for 'viol' or 'fiddle,' and 'violin' means 'little viol.' Now my name in Italian is 'violone,' which means 'biggest viol'; and 'violoncello' really means 'little violone.' "

"I see," said Alice; "it's all clear now—only I thought your name was 'bass viol.' "

"So it is. You see, I have several names. In Italy they call me 'violone' or 'contrabasso,' and in your country 'bass viol' or 'double bass.' But most people call me simply 'bass,' because it's easier to say.   And now we'd better stop talking and listen to the music.   It's a quartet by Mozart—one of his best."

It was indeed exquisite music, and Alice marveled that the four automatons—mere pieces of machinery—could produce such lovely sounds, even with the aid of four fine instruments.   It was not like the music of the full orchestra—not so loud and rich; but it made up for that by its purity and delicacy.   Alice listened attentively throughout the performance of the quartet, but when it was finished she was ready with a lot of new questions.

"Why," she demanded of her friend the Bass, "do they have different kinds of fiddles in a quartet?   Why not four violins or four violas or four violoncellos?"

"Ah," said the Bass, "we have instruments of different sizes partly in order to give variety of tone color and partly in order to increase the compass of the quartet.   Do you know what 'compass' means?"

Alice shook her head.

" 'Compass,' " explained the Bass, "means the number of tones, from the lowest to the highest, that an instrument or a group of instruments can produce. Now the piano can produce all the notes of the scale—over seven octaves—but the orchestral instruments have much smaller compasses. So in order to produce the entire scale we have to combine several instruments of different sizes, the smaller ones playing the high notes, the larger ones the low notes. For, as a general rule, the larger an instrument is, the lower its pitch."

"No wonder you have such a deep voice!" Alice exclaimed, gazing with new interest at the enormous bulk of the Bass.

"My voice is the lowest of all, except the double bassoon and bass tuba," he said proudly. "I can sing the lowest E on the piano. But I haven't finished explaining about the compass of the string quartet. The violin, as you probably know, can play as high as the highest notes on the piano, but it can't go lower than the G below Middle C. Do you know what Middle C is?"

"Oh, yes," said Alice. "It's the white key just to the left of the two black keys just to the left of the keyhole."

The Bass chuckled. "I see you know how to find it. Well, then, the viola can't go as high as the violin, but it can go five tones lower—to the C an octave below Middle C; and the 'cello can go an octave below the viola. So between them they have a compass of six octaves—and with a scale of six octaves you can make a lot of music. Of course, for orchestral work you need a still larger scale, and a very strong bass besides; that's where I come in. I can go nearly an octave lower than the 'cello, and my low tones are fuller and heavier, too, so that's why I'm one of the most important instruments in the orchestra." The Bass sat up very straight and certainly looked extremely important.

Alice was duly impressed, but her mind was still teeming with questions.

"Why," she inquired, "are there two violins in a quartet? I should think one would be enough, since there's only one viola and one 'cello."

"Well," said the Bass, "in the first place, if there were only one violin it wouldn't be a quartet—it would be a trio; and a trio isn't so satisfactory as a quartet, partly because most music is written in four-part harmony, and partly because the tone of the 'cello is stronger than the tone of the violin. So we have two violins, a first violin and a second violin, to keep the balance."

"What's the difference between a first violin and a second violin?" Alice asked. "They look exactly alike."

"So they are," said the Bass. "The only difference is that the first violin usually plays higher than the second. Do you go to church?"

The question was so unexpected that Alice was a little disconcerted. "Wh—why, yes—of course," she stammered.

"Then you've probably heard a vocal quartet —a quartet of singers—two women and two men."

"Yes, indeed," said Alice. "We have a quartet choir at our church every Sunday."

"And do you know which voice sings the highest part?"

"The soprano."

"And the next highest?"

"The alto."

"And the next?"

"The tenor."

"And the lowest?"

"The bass."

"Quite right. Now, then, a string quartet is

just like a vocal quartet: the first violin is the soprano, the second violin is the alto, the viola's the tenor, and the 'cello's the bass. And a symphony orchestra is simply a group of three quartets—a string quartet, a wood-wind quartet, and a brass quartet—with a few extra instruments and a lot of drums and cymbals and things thrown in for good measure. I dare say you thought an orchestra was a frightfully complicated affair, but you see it's really quite simple."

"I *am* beginning to understand it a little better," Alice confessed. "But there's lots and lots of it that I still don't know about; for instance, the wood-wind quartet—what is that?"

"You shall learn all about it in due time," said the Bass. "But now I want to introduce you to some of the fiddles. They've finished their rehearsal, so come along and we'll interview them before they go home."

CHAPTER IV

A QUARTET OUT OF TUNE

THE Bass Viol led Alice through a door at one side of the auditorium and down a corridor that brought them to a room behind the stage. There they found the four instruments who had just finished their rehearsal. They were busily engaged in removing the powdered rosin that had accumulated on their strings, carrying on meanwhile an animated conversation. So absorbed were they in their own affairs that they did not see Alice and the Bass Viol enter the room.

"Stop here a moment," whispered the Bass, halting just inside the door. "Do you see that handsome amber-colored violin—the one who is talking to the 'Cello? He is the leader of the quartet and the Principal First Violin of the orchestra. We call him the Concertmaster. Distinguished-looking fiddle, isn't he?"

"Yes," Alice agreed; "but he looks rather conceited."

"Well, perhaps he is," the Bass chuckled. "You see, he comes of one of the first families of Cremona—the Stradivari—and he's very proud of it."

"Cremona?" said Alice. "Where is that?"

"Cremona," replied the Bass, "is a little town in Italy where all the finest violins come from— the Stradivari, the Amati, the Guarneri, and many others. Now the Second Violin—that modest looking brown one—is not from Cremona: he's a Tyrolean. He's a thoroughly good sort—plenty of tone and all that; but he hasn't got the grand manner of the Cremonese. It's the same with the Viola; he's a nice fellow, but not an aristocrat. He claims to be a Gagliano, but the fact of the matter is that his pedigree has been lost, so nobody knows whether he really is or not."

"Maybe that's why he's so sad," Alice suggested.

The Bass smiled.

"Possibly," he admitted; "but I'm afraid that doesn't account for the fact that all the other violas are sad, too. I think sadness must run in the family. Now, it's different with the 'cellos. They're nearly always in high spirits, even those who have lost their pedigrees. This one is particularly high-spirited. He's French—a Vuillaume—and has the true Gallic temperament. He's well thought of in the community; but, of course, he isn't a 'Strad.' However, I'd better introduce you to them, or they'll be going home."

The Bass escorted Alice across the room, and addressed the First Violin.

"Tony," he said, "allow me to present a young friend of mine who has come to pay us a visit: Mr. Stradivari, Miss—er——"

"Alice," said that young lady, politely.

The Violin bowed ceremoniously. Although his bearing was proud, his manner was gracious and polished. When he spoke it was with a slight foreign accent and in a remarkably clear and resonant voice—a voice so melodious that he seemed almost to be singing.

"We are honored," he said gravely. "The young lady is a musician?"

"Not yet," said Alice, "but I hope to be some day. I'm learning to play the piano."

"Ah!" said the Violin, "the piano. A useful instrument but veree mechanical—veree. You should learn to play one of us."

"I should like to, very much," said Alice timidly; "but I'm afraid it would be awfully difficult. I don't see how——"

"Excuse me," the Bass interrupted. "Do you mind if I present these other gentlemen; I'm rather pressed for time. Mr. Stainer, the Second Violin; Mr.—er—Gagliano, our Principal Viola; Mr. Vuillaume, First 'Cello. Gentlemen, Miss Alice."

The fiddles bowed and Alice curtsied. Ordinarily Alice hated to curtsy; none of the little girls she knew ever did it. But her mother, who was very old-fashioned, had insisted that Alice must learn to curtsy, and now she was rather glad she had, for it seemed just the proper thing to do on this occasion.

"And now," said the Bass, "I must be off. I'm late for an appointment already, so I'll just leave the young lady in your charge—you'll take good care of her, I know. I warn you, she's a wonder when it comes to asking questions; so be prepared to tell her the stories of your lives.

Good-bye—see you later." So saying, he waddled across the room and disappeared through
the door, leaving Alice a trifle ill-at-ease among
so many strangers. But the quartet were very
kind, and did their best to make her feel at home.

"If you will tell us what it is you would like
to know about us," the First Violin suggested,
"we shall be happy to inform you to the best of
our ability."

"Thank you very much," said Alice; "but, oh,
dear! There are so many questions I want to
ask that I don't know where to begin."

"Then, suppose I begin at the beginning and
tell you everything about us that I think would
interest you."

"Oh, yes—please do," said Alice.

"And if you think of any questions as we go
along," the Violin continued, "don't hesitate to
ask them. That will make it easier for me to
tell you just the things you want to know.

"Now, to begin—we are called 'stringed instruments.' That is because our tone, or sound,
comes from the vibration of strings stretched
very tightly over a resonant sound box. Do you
know what 'vibration' means?"

Alice shook her head doubtfully.

"Then I will try to explain it. Suppose you

lie in a hammock and let somebody swing you. You go first to one side, then to the other—right, left; right, left—just like that, don't you? If the hammock is a big one you swing slowly; if the hammock is a little one, or if it is stretched very tight, you swing faster; and if they push you hard you swing farther to the right and left, don't you?"

Alice nodded her assent to this proposition.

"All right, then," the Violin continued, "that is vibration. But it is very slow. Now, can you imagine a hammock swinging from side to side so fast that your eye cannot follow it—three or four hundred times a second?"

Alice's eyes grew big. "O-oh," she said, "it would make me dizzy!"

"It would indeed," said the Violin; "but, of course, no hammocks can swing that fast. However, a violin string is like a hammock— fastened securely at each end, with the middle free to vibrate, or swing from side to side; and that is what happens when you pluck it or draw a bow across it. But because the string is so short and stretched so tight it vibrates very fast —so fast that it makes a sound. Now, the tighter a string is stretched, or the shorter it is, the faster it vibrates; and the faster it vibrates, the higher the sound it gives out." He plucked his second string. "That," he said, "is the A above Middle C, and it vibrates four hundred and forty times a second."

"Why," said Alice, amazed, "I didn't know that anything could move as fast as that!"

"Pooh!" said the Violin, "that's nothing. The next A above this one vibrates twice as fast—eight hundred and eighty times a second, and the A above that one vibrates one thousand seven hundred and sixty times a second. Because each time you go up an octave the number of vibrations is doubled."

"But how do you play the high notes?" asked Alice.

"By shortening one of the strings—generally the first one, called the E-string—so that it vibrates more rapidly."

"But I don't see how you can shorten it," Alice objected. "It's fastened tight at both ends."

"That is true," said the Strad; "but it can be shortened, just the same. I will show you how."

He plucked his first string, producing a sharp but musical sound. "That," he said, "is E—the second E above Middle C. The entire string is now vibrating, from the bridge to this little ridge of wood, which we call the 'nut,' at the upper end of the fingerboard. Now, just place the first finger of your left hand on the string here, close to the nut, and press down hard."

Alice did as she was told, whereupon the Strad again plucked his E-string, this time producing a higher tone than before.

"There," said the Strad, "you see? That tone is F—a half tone higher than the open string; and you produced it by shortening the string."

"But I didn't shorten it," said Alice; "I only pressed my finger on it."

The Strad smiled and patiently explained: "Pressing your finger on the string shortens it, to all intents and purposes. It can only vibrate between the bridge and the point where your finger presses it against the fingerboard; so the part of the string that vibrates is shorter—and the rest doesn't count."

"Now I understand," said Alice, greatly interested. "And I suppose that if I press my second finger on the string it will give a still higher note?"

"Exactly," said the Strad; "your second finger will play G or G-sharp, your third finger A-flat or A, and your fourth finger B-flat or B. If you wish to play higher than that you must

slide your hand along the neck to a higher position—that is, nearer the bridge. In that way
you can reach all the notes, right up to the end
of the fingerboard."

"Isn't it very hard to know just where to place
your fingers?" Alice inquired. "There doesn't
seem to be anything to guide you."

"It *is* difficult," the Strad admitted. "It takes
a lot of practice; but it can be learned, just as a
blind man can learn to find his way about his
house—and then, of course, it seems quite easy."

"Now," he went on, "I want to explain to you
about harmonics. They are very important,
because they will help you to understand the
wind instruments when you meet them."

"Suppose you place your finger here on
my E-string, exactly halfway between the bridge
and the nut—so; and, instead of pressing down
hard, merely touch the string lightly."

Alice did so, and the Strad passed his bow
across the string, producing a high flute-like
tone, very soft and clear.

"That," he said, "is a 'harmonic.' It is
caused by dividing the string into two equal
parts with a light touch of your finger which
leaves *both* parts free to vibrate. The tone produced is an octave higher than the open string.

Now, if you touch the string at the proper place, it will also vibrate in three, four, or even five, equal sections, producing still higher 'harmonics'; and as these 'harmonics' are very clear and penetrating they are very often used. But I have explained them to you chiefly because, as I said before, they will help you to understand how the wind instruments produce their tones. Now I will tell you something about the bow, which is very important, for a fiddle without a bow would be almost entirely useless. As you have seen, my strings can be plucked with the finger, like those of a guitar or banjo; indeed, they are sometimes played that way in the orchestra—*pizzicato,* we call it—but that is only for special effects. Most of the time my strings are set in vibration by rubbing them with the hair of a bow, the hair being covered with powdered rosin to increase the friction.

"There are many ways of using the bow. It can be drawn slowly and evenly, so that it produces a long, sustained tone, or it can be moved very rapidly back and forth, in what is called *tremolo*. It can strike the strings with abrupt hammer-strokes, called *martellato;* it can dance upon them gracefully in *spiccato;* it can caress them in smooth, flowing *legato* passages—and do many ·other things, too numerous to mention." The Strad illustrated each method of bowing as he described it, greatly to Alice's admiration.

"Why, it looks quite easy," she said; "I believe I could do that."

"Try," said the Strad, smiling indulgently as he handed her the bow.

Alice took it and endeavored to imitate the manner in which the Strad had held it, but found, to her dismay, that the light and slender stick of wood seemed to grow suddenly heavy and clumsy in her hand; and when she attempted to draw it across the strings of the fiddle it trembled ludicrously and brought forth only a succession of miserable squeaks. The Strad laughed good-humoredly.

"It's not so easy as it looks, you see. Now you can appreciate how difficult it is for all the fiddles in an orchestra—fifty or sixty of them—to bow together in perfect unison, as if they were parts of a machine, as they do in all good orchestras."

"It's wonderful!" Alice exclaimed. "I don't see how they ever do it. But tell me—why are there so many fiddles in an orchestra?"

"In order to obtain the proper balance of

tone," replied the Strad. "Our tone is softer and less penetrating than that of the wind instruments, so if there were not a great many of us we would be overpowered by the wood-wind and brasses. In a well-balanced orchestra the 'strings,' as we are generally called, outnumber all the other instruments by about two to one— that is, there are about sixty 'strings' to about thirty wood-wind, brass, and percussion instruments. So it's easy to see that we are by far the most important branch of the family." The Strad drew himself up, a trifle pompously, and Alice said to herself: "There, he *is* conceited." Aloud she asked innocently: "Is that what makes you the most important—that there are so many of you?"

"Certainly not!" said the Strad indignantly. "We are the most important because our tone is the most agreeable to listen to, and because we have a greater compass than any other group of instruments and can play more complicated passages. Also we can play longer without getting tired, and we have the greatest range, from very soft to very loud. But perhaps the chief reason is our enormous emotional range—if you understand what that means."

"I'm afraid I don't," said Alice.

"It means," the Violin explained, "that we can express more different emotions than any other group of instruments. We can be gay; we can be sad; we can laugh; we can weep; we can threaten; we can plead. We can make you think of fairies dancing in the moonlight, or of desolate mountains swept by icy winds; of shepherds guarding their flocks, or of demons riding madly through the night. Of course, no one of us alone can do all this. My duty is usually to play the brilliant or romantic or tender passages. If the composer wants to express sadness he generally gives the principal part to the violas; and if his theme is bold and vigorous, it is most often the 'cellos who play it, while fear and anger are best expressed by the ominous low tones of the basses. The basses, though, can be quite comic at times. They are so big and clumsy that when they attempt rapid, graceful passages the effect is often quite funny. You should hear them imitate elephants dancing the minuet, as they do in 'The Carnival of the Animals,' by Saint-Saëns."

"Oh, I should love to!" said Alice, laughing.

"Now that I come to think of it, you *may* near them—this very evening," said the Strad. "There will be a concert by the full orchestra.

and 'The Carnival of the Animals' is on the programme. We shall expect you."

"I shall come, with pleasure," said Alice. "But," she added, turning to the Second Violin, who up to this time had remained modestly in the background, "you haven't told me what *you* do in the orchestra."

The Second Violin appeared embarrassed.

"Why, m-my task," he stammered, "is rather a humble one. Generally all I have to do is to fill in the harmony, or to help my friend here, the First Violin, to carry the melody. Occasionally I have a solo passage, but not very often. As a rule my duties are comparatively unimportant."

He seemed so modest and unassuming that Alice could not help feeling a little sorry for him.

"I'm sure," she said, wishing to cheer him up, "that you are just as important as any of the others, even if your part isn't so—so showy."

"You're quite right," interposed the 'Cello; "this chap's humility is simply preposterous. He's as necessary to the orchestra as any of us, but just because he's called 'Second Volin' he thinks he doesn't amount to a hill of beans. He ought to cultivate a little decent vanity."

"It wouldn't be of any use," said the Viola, gloomily. "If he did he'd only become a first violin, and then where should we be?"

The Strad looked as if he were somewhat nettled by the Viola's remark, but he apparently decided to ignore it, for presently he smiled, rather haughtily, and said, with the evident intention of changing the subject:

"There is one more point to which we should call the young lady's attention: I refer to the *sordino,* or mute."

He held up, so that Alice could see it, a queer little black object which looked somewhat like a very short comb with only three teeth.

"This," he explained, "when placed on the bridge of a fiddle, makes its tone sound softer and thinner and rather sad." As he spoke he fixed the mute upon his own bridge, and instantly his voice sounded more gentle and subdued.

"Oh, I love that!" Alice exclaimed. "Why don't you use it all the time?"

"Because you would soon grow tired of it, as you do of too much sugar. Besides, it weakens my voice too much; I shouldn't be able to hold my own against the other instruments." He removed the mute, and his voice again became strong and clear. "There, that's better, after all, isn't it?"

"Well, I s'pose so," Alice conceded. "But your voice sounded so soft and sweet with the mute."

"It's strange," observed the 'Cello, "how many people like their music soft and sweet. I can't understand it. Lots of them admire my soft, rich low tones and don't care at all for my brilliant upper register, which is really the best part of my voice. Their ears are too delicate— they ought to wear ear muffs when they go to a concert."

"They should, indeed—if there are any 'cellos on the programme," said the Viola, plaintively. "You really are a noisy lot—always trying to play louder than the rest of the orchestra combined."

"Oh, shut up!" snapped the 'Cello. "What do you know about it? You haven't the spirit of an asthmatic mouth organ. If I couldn't play louder than a whole section of violas, I'd——"

"Gentlemen! Gentlemen!" interposed the Second Violin, "you're out of tune. Tony, will you give the A?"

The First Violin plucked his second string,

and the 'Cello sulkily turned one of the pegs that projected from the sides of his head until his own A-string was in tune with that of the Violin.

"As usual, he's much too sharp," grumbled the Viola.

"Well, well," said the Strad, mollifyingly, "he's not the only one at fault: you must admit you're a trifle flat. Now, tune up, and let's have no more of this discord, or our guest will have a poor opinion of us."

The Viola did as he was told, and harmony was restored, much to the relief of Alice, who had feared for a moment that the antagonists might come to blows. As they now appeared to be once more on friendly terms, she decided to take her departure, for she was anxious to visit the other instruments while there was still time.

"Thank you very much for all you have told me," she said to the quartet. "I shall try not to forget it. And now, if you will tell me how to find the place where the wind instruments live, I think I had better go."

"We are sorry that you can't stay longer," said the First Violin, "but we shall hope to see you in the audience this evening. Meanwhile, if you'll allow me, I shall be happy to see you as far as the next village, where you will find the flutes and clarinets and all their relatives of the wood-wind family. It isn't far—we can walk there in a few minutes."

"It's very good of you to take so much trouble," said Alice; and saying good-bye to the other fiddles she accompanied the Strad out of the auditorium and down the road that led to the home of the wood-wind instruments.

CHAPTER V

A TEA PARTY IN PANOPOLIS

LICE and the Violin walked at a brisk pace and soon had left behind them the village of Fiddladelphia. Their way led them through a pleasant wood of stately oaks and beeches, from which they emerged at last upon a grassy common within view of another village.

"There is our destination," said the Violin: "the village of Panopolis."

"What a queer name!" Alice exclaimed. "What does it mean?"

"It means 'The City of Pan.' Pan, you know, according to the old Greek legend, was a half-god—a jolly sort of chap, with the head and body of a man and the legs and horns of a goat and he is supposed to have invented the first wind instrument. He fell in love with a beautiful nymph named Syrinx, but she was afraid of his horns and his hoofs and would have nothing to do with him. So Pan changed her into a reed, and then from the reed he made a pipe on which he played the most exquisite music. And as all the wood-wind instruments are supposed to be descended from the pipe of Pan, they regard him as a sort of patron saint of their family, and have named their village in his honor. But here we are at the home of my friend the Oboe. He's a charming fellow, and takes pleasure in answering questions by the hour—but I ought to warn you that in some ways he's just a little—er—queer. Nothing serious, of course—perfectly harmless and all that, but—how shall I say?—a trifle eccentric. He has strange notions about pets, and takes great pride in his ancestry, and all that sort of thing. But—well, you shall see."

They had arrived at a high hedge enclosing a lawn, in the middle of which was a tiny rustic cottage with a thatched roof. Passing through a low lych gate they found themselves in the

midst of a large flock of sheep, who stopped
grazing and looked at them stupidly. Alice
hesitated. The sheep looked harmless enough,
but she had never encountered so many of them
before, and she wasn't sure that they mightn't
butt. The Violin reassured her.

"Don't mind the sheep," he said; "they're
quite gentle. My friend is so fond of them
that he always has a lot of them about. I told
you that he had queer notions about pets; but,
you see, he comes of a pastoral family—that is,
his earliest ancestors were played by shepherds
as they tended their flocks—so his fondness for
sheep is inherited. He says they make him feel
at home. To this day, there's nothing a thor-
oughbred oboe likes to play so well as a simple
pastoral melody, such as the shepherds of olden
times used to improvise to amuse themselves
during their long vigils. His voice has a
plaintive, wistful quality that makes one think
of vast lonely spaces, with no sound but the sigh-
ing of the wind in the grasses, and perhaps, far
away, a shepherd's pipe. However, the Oboe
can also be gay. He can play the merriest dance
tunes and the jolliest songs; and he is also particularly good at Oriental music."

By this time they had reached the door of the

cottage upon which the Violin rapped with his bow. It was opened almost immediately by a queer little instrument about two feet tall, whom the Violin introduced to Alice as the First Oboe. His body consisted of a tube of black wood, about half-an-inch in diameter at the top, but growing gradually larger until at the bottom it flared out into a bell-shaped opening about two inches wide. Down its front, like a row of waistcoat buttons, were six round holes, and attached to it at various points was a complicated system of rods and keys and levers, all made of silver. Projecting from the top of its head, like a feather from its cap, was a slender stem which ended in a sort of wedge-shaped contrivance.

The Oboe welcomed his visitors in a rather thin and nasal voice which reminded Alice of the sounds she herself had often produced with the aid of a comb and a piece of tissue paper. He assured Alice that he would do his best to make her visit both pleasant and instructive, whereupon the Violin left them, to return to Fiddladelphia. Alice lost no time in beginning her quest for knowledge.

"Now, please tell me," she said, "all about yourself and the other members of your family

—how you are played, and what you do in the orchestra, and everything."

"Well," said the Oboe, "my family is a large and very ancient one. I can tell you about myself, but I think that the best way for you to learn the characteristics and peculiarities of my relatives is to meet them all personally. Would you like to do that?"

"Oh, yes!" Alice replied with enthusiasm. "That is, if it will not be too much trouble for you."

"It will be the easiest thing in the world," the Oboe assured her. "It happens, fortunately, that I have invited them all for tea this afternoon. They will be here shortly, so if you will be good enough to join our party you can make their acquaintance without the least inconvenience to anybody."

Alice accepted the invitation with thanks.

"Then that's settled," said the Oboe. "Now, while we are waiting for the others, I may as well pass the time by telling you something about our respective duties in the orchestra. Shall we sit out on the lawn? It's very pleasant there—and I like to keep an eye on my sheep."

The Oboe led the way to a large maple tree in

whose shade were several rustic seats, on one of which Alice sat down, while her host reclined as gracefully as his unbending physique permitted on the grass beside her.

"The wood-wind section of the orchestra," he began, "is composed as a rule of flutes, oboes, clarinets, and bassoons. Together we form a quartet similar to the string quartet, with soprano, alto, tenor, and bass voices. In our quartet the Flute is the soprano, I am the alto, the Clarinet is the tenor, and the Bassoon the bass. But our quartet differs from the string quartet in one important respect: while they have from ten to twenty instruments of each kind—first violins, second violins, violas, and so forth—we have only two or three. The reason for that is that our tone is so peculiar and so penetrating that even a single flute or oboe or clarinet can make itself heard over the whole body of strings."

"But I thought you said your family was a very large one," said Alice.

"So I did," said the Oboe, "but I expressed myself inaccurately. What I meant to say was that our family was one of many branches; for while in numbers the wood-wind instruments are greatly inferior to the strings, there are more different kinds of them. In addition to the four I have named, there are several others which, although they are not regular members of our section, frequently help us out, particularly in the performance of modern compositions. There is, for instance, the Flute's little brother, the Piccolo; and the Clarinet's big brother, the Bass Clarinet. And I have a cousin—the English Horn—and a great-uncle—the Double Bassoon. Besides, there are the Bass Flute, the Oboe d'Amore, the Basset Horn and the Double Bass Clarinet—but we see very little of them; they lead a retired life and seldom appear in public.

"Now that you know the names of my relatives," the Oboe continued, "I shall try to give you an idea of how we are played. All wind instruments, you must know, are alike in one respect: that is, their tone is caused by the vibration of a column of air in a tube, just as the tone of all stringed instruments is caused by the vibration of a string stretched over a resonant box. But wind instruments differ from one another in the means by which their column of air is made to vibrate. In my own case, it is set in motion by the vibration of a 'reed' which is held between the player's lips and through which he blows his breath. A 'reed' is simply a narrow strip of cane, shaved down to a very thin edge at one end; but if you will look carefully at my reed"—he pointed to the "feather in his cap"—"you will see that it consists of two strips of cane bound together so that the thin ends are left free to vibrate. For that reason, I am called a 'double-reed' instrument. The English horn, bassoon, double bassoon, and oboe d'amore are also double-reed instruments; but the clarinet, bass clarinet, and basset horn have only a single reed which vibrates against a wedge-shaped mouthpiece, while the flute and piccolo have no reed at all. Their air column is set in motion simply by blowing across an opening near one end of the tube."

The Oboe paused a moment for breath, and Alice took advantage of the opportunity to ask a question. How, she inquired, did one produce all the different tones on a wind instrument—the high ones and the low ones?

"The pitch of our tone—that is, whether it is high or low—depends on the length of the vibrating column of air," the Oboe replied, "just as the pitch of a tone on the violin depends on the length of the vibrating string. Now, I am about two feet long, and the lowest tone that I can play is the B-flat below Middle C. To

produce that tone all these holes which you see
in my body must be closed by the player's fingers. To produce higher tones the player raises
his fingers, or uncovers other holes by means of
these keys and levers, which shortens the vibrating column of air, just as if the tube had been
cut off at the point where the hole is uncovered.
It is worth remembering, by the way, that if you
double the length of a tube you lower its pitch
one octave. Thus the bassoon, which is four
times as long as I am, can play two octaves
lower; and the double bassoon, which is eight
times as long as I am, can play an octave lower
than the bassoon. The double bassoon has the
deepest voice of all the bass instruments; he can
sing the lowest C on the piano. But I'm afraid
we are wandering from our subject. What you
want to know is what we do in the orchestra, is
it not?"

"Yes," said Alice, "but I also want to know
what each of you looks like and how his voice
sounds."

"Well," said the Oboe, "you will not have to
wait much longer for that information, for here
come the first of our guests—the Flute and his
little brother, the Piccolo."

Alice looked in the direction of the gate, and

saw two instruments advancing across the lawn. The larger one was about as tall as the Oboe, but his body, instead of tapering, was the same size from top to bottom, and no reed projected from the top of his head; but on the right side of his face was a hole which looked like a single eye. Like the Oboe, however, he was provided with six finger-holes and a number of keys. His companion was exactly like him in every respect except that he was not quite half as tall. Altogether, they were an interesting pair, but the most striking thing about them, to Alice, was the fact that they appeared to be made entirely of silver.

"Why," she whispered to the Oboe, "I thought they were wood-wind instruments."

"So they are," said the Oboe. "You see, they used to be made of wood, until it was found that silver gave a better tone and truer pitch; so we still consider them members of our family. Don't you think them handsome?"

Alice had no chance to reply, for by this time the Flute was greeting the Oboe cordially in a soft, velvety voice that sounded like rippling water. His manner was gentle and polite, though a trifle reserved. Alice thought him charming, and gave him one of her very best curtsies when the Oboe presented him to her. The Piccolo was then introduced—and proved to be quite a different sort of person. His manners were not of the best, and his voice was the highest that Alice had ever heard. It resembled that of the Flute, but lacked its softness and gentleness. It was piercing and impudent, and when he laughed, as he often did, it was shrill and unpleasant. Altogether, he seemed the sort of instrument who would delight in practical jokes, such as slipping up behind people and shrieking in their ears.

"Pleased to meet you," he said, seizing Alice's hand and giving it a violent squeeze. "What do you think of our town and all my jolly family? I think they're a gloomy, low-toned lot, if you want my opinion"—and he laughed so shrilly that Alice involuntarily put her hands over her ears. The Piccolo appeared not to notice her action, however; nor did he seem to expect an answer to his rather embarrassing question. At all events, Alice was spared the necessity of replying, for at that moment two more guests arrived. One of these Alice at first took to be another oboe, but as he drew nearer she saw that, though he was of about the same height as his host, there were several important differences between them. His bell, she noticed, was larger than the Oboe's, and his body, like the Flute's, did not taper, but was of equal thickness from end to end. He had finger-holes and keys like the Oboe, but his mouthpiece was quite different, for it was nearly as thick as his body, and was beveled off at the end into a wedge, against one side of which a single reed was fixed by means of a silver band adjusted with thumb-screws.

"This," said the Oboe to Alice, "is my kinsman the Clarinet. We are supposed—by people who don't know us very well—to look somewhat alike; but I'm sure you would never mistake one of us for the other, would you?"

"I hope not," said Alice. "Now that I have seen you together I think I shall always be able to tell you apart; but at first I *almost* thought you were twin brothers."

"Such bright eyes could not long be deceived," said the Clarinet, gallantly. His voice was rich and full and his manner gracious. He reminded Alice somewhat of the First Violin, though he was less brilliant and rather more romantic.

The Clarinet's companion, the Bass Clarinet, was then presented. He was the strangest looking instrument Alice had yet seen. His body was similar to the Clarinet's, but longer, and his bell, which was made of silver, curved upward and outward, so that Alice could look down into it. His mouthpiece, instead of being attached directly to the top of his tube, was connected with it by a neck of silver about a foot long, curved so that it projected backward at right angles to his body. Alice estimated that if he were stretched out in a straight line, instead of being bent up at the bottom and down at the top, he would be just twice as long as the Clarinet.

"That means," she said to herself, recalling what the Oboe had said about the length of tubes, "that his voice is an octave lower than the Clarinet's." That soon proved to be the case, for when the Bass Clarinet spoke it was in a low, rich voice, deeper and more resonant than the Clarinet's and with more of the "reedy" comb-and-tissue-paper quality peculiar to reed instruments. He was rather grave and solemn, and Alice decided that he belonged, like the Viola, to the company of sad instruments.

The next guests to arrive were even more remarkable in appearance than the Bass Clarinet. There were three of them, the smallest being evidently the Oboe's cousin of whom Alice had heard, for he resembled the Oboe closely in several features. His body tapered toward the top, like the Oboe's, but he was about half as tall again, and his bell was bulb-shaped. His double reed was connected with his body by a slender metal stem about five inches long, which was bent slightly backward.

The Oboe presented him:

"Permit me—my cousin, the English Horn."

"How do you do?" Alice inquired politely.

The English Horn bowed ceremoniously but said nothing. Alice thought he must be bashful and tried to put him at ease.

"Do you come from London?" she asked. "My father's been there. It must be a wonderful city."

The English Horn looked extremely uncomfortable, and murmured something in a foreign tongue, whereupon all the other instruments burst out laughing. Alice looked at them in astonishment.

" Why, he's never been in England in his life," the Oboe explained. "He can't even speak a word of English."

"But I thought you said he was an English horn." Alice was completely puzzled.

"It *is* rather confusing, I admit," said the Oboe. "Why he should be known as an 'English horn' when he's neither English nor a horn is a bit of a mystery. He's really a tenor oboe and comes from the same country as myself— whatever that may be. Some say it is Arabia, others claim that we hail from ancient Egypt. In any case, we certainly are not of English origin. But somehow or other, many years ago, my cousin acquired the name of *cor anglais,* which is French for 'English horn,' and it has stuck to him ever since. He's really very nice, although he's always dejected; and though he can't speak English he can sing in any language."

Again the English Horn murmured something which Alice did not understand, so she simply smiled and nodded in a friendly way. He was certainly the saddest of all the instruments. His voice was low and vibrant, full of pathos, and with a kind of veiled quality, as if it came from far away. Like the Oboe, it suggested the lonely shepherd's pipe, but such a *very* lonely, plaintive shepherd's pipe that Alice could think of nothing but a shepherd who, like little Bo-peep, had lost his sheep.

"Now," said the Oboe, "let me make you acquainted with the last—but not the least—of my relatives: my uncle, the Bassoon, and my great-uncle, the Double Bassoon."

The two instruments acknowledged the introduction with much dignity. The Bassoon was a gentleman of rather pompous demeanor. His body consisted of a tube eight feet long, which, however, was doubled up so that he stood only about four feet high. His bell, which did not flare out like those of the Oboe and Clarinet, was at the top instead of the bottom of his body, and his reed was attached to the smaller end of his tube by a curved metal shank similar to that of the Bass Clarinet, but much slenderer. His voice was very low and rather gruff, and he seemed to be a person of variable mood, for at times he was as solemn as a judge, while at others he was quite comical.

The Double Bassoon resembled the Bassoon in most respects, except that he was much larger and even more solemn. He seldom tried to be funny, and his voice was a mere rumble—which was no wonder, for he was sixteen feet long. In spite of the fact that his tube had been bent into four folds in order to make him less cumbersome, he towered over Alice to a height of

nearly six feet. He had a bell of metal like
that of the Bass Clarinet, but it was attached to
the upper end of his tube and curved downward.

All the guests having now arrived, the Oboe
invited them into his little thatched cottage,
where a delicious tea was served. Alice was
quite hungry, and in a remarkably short time
had consumed a large quantity of tea and cake.
The instruments, however, in spite of the fact
that each held a teacup solemnly in his hand,
neither drank nor ate. This strange conduct
perplexed Alice, and presently she sought an ex-
planation of it.

"Don't you like tea?" she inquired of the Piccolo, who was standing beside her.

"I love it," he replied. "We all do."

"Then why don't you drink it?" Alice de-
nanded.

"Drink it!" shrieked the Piccolo. "Who
ever heard of such a thing? Why, it's wet—it
would be the ruin of us!"

"Then why do you bother to have it?" Alice
was completely mystified.

"Oh, it's quite the thing to do," said the Piccolo. Then he added confidentially: "You

know, there's nothing that gives one as much assurance as being able to handle a teacup in a drawing-room; besides, tea is so soothing to the nerves"—and with a shrill giggle he walked away, leaving Alice to wonder what on earth he meant.

CHAPTER VI

THE BRASSYDALE BAND

ALICE was enjoying the tea party enormously, but the musical chimes of a large grandfather clock warned her that the hour was growing late and that she must be on her way if she wished to call on the other instruments before dinner time. So she drew her host aside and begged him to excuse her, which he very graciously did, accompanying her as far as the gate to point out the way.

"You can't mistake the road," he said. "Just take the first turning to the right and then keep straight ahead, and you will soon come to Brassydale, where the brass instruments live. It's a small village, separated from this one only by the Wood. I'm sorry not to go with you, but I can't very well leave my other guests."

"Of course not," said Alice. "Anyhow, I'm sure I can find the way. So good-bye—and thank you very much. I've had a delightful time."

Alice followed the road the Oboe had indicated, and soon found herself in the Wood, which proved to be a beautiful shady park. The path lay along the bank of a little brook which rippled and murmured and tinkled delightfully. Alice had never heard such a musical brook. Indeed, it seemed to be singing a distinct and charming melody, which Alice, after listening carefully for a few moments, was able to hum along with it.

Alice thought the song beautiful and made up her mind never to forget it, so she kept humming it over and over to herself as she went along.

Thus far she had found the path quite easy to follow, but presently she came to a place where it divided, one branch continuing straight ahead, the other turning off to the right. She hesitated, and was looking about for some guide or signpost to tell her which branch to take when she spied a small tent a few yards back from the path. Before it on a log sat a forlorn-looking instrument which resembled a huge Dutch pipe with a very thick stem. It was about eighteen inches high, and its body, which was made of brass, tapered upward to a slender neck that was bent sharply backward and had a clarinet mouthpiece attached to it, while the other end flared out into a large upturned bell.

Alice approached the tent and addressed its proprietor.

"Excuse me," she said, "can you tell me which of those paths leads to Brassydale?"

"Yes," replied the instrument, surlily.

Alice waited expectantly, but as he did not seem disposed to say anything further, she finally asked, as politely as possible:

"Well, then, which path *does* lead there?"

The instrument stared at her morosely. "It's no use going there," he said, at length. "They won't let you stay. They always turn *me* out —and you're certainly not as much of a brass instrument as I am."

His voice was hoarse, as if he might have

caught cold from sleeping in the woods, and he appeared so miserable that Alice couldn't help feeling sorry for him.

"Why do they turn you out?" she asked.

"They claim I'm a wood-wind instrument, because I've got a reed like a clarinet, and they say I ought to go and live in Panopolis."

"Then why don't you?"

"Oh, I've tried to, time and again, but it's no use. The wood-wind instruments say I belong in Brassydale, because my body is made of brass. So at last I got this tent and pitched it here, halfway between the two villages. It's damp and rather lonely, but at least they can't turn me out of it. So you'd better get yourself a tent at once, and save a lot of bother. I'll show you how to pitch it."

"Thank you very much," said Alice, "but I'm only a visitor, so I think I'll go on to Brassydale. They'll surely let me stay a little while. I think it's a shame, though, the way they treat you."

"I'm glad to see you have some sense of justice," said the instrument. "What is your name?"

Alice told him.

"Mine," he said, "is Saxophone."

"It's no use going there," he said.

"Oh!" cried Alice, "I've heard of you, often. Do you belong to the orchestra, too?"

"I'm not a regular member; they only let me play in it occasionally. They say I'm too unrefined to associate with them—the snobs!"

"Why," said Alice, "I don't think that's a bit nice of them. I'm sure you're——" she hesitated. The Saxophone had sunk into a gloomy meditation, and she decided that she had better leave him to ponder his grievances in solitude.

"If you will kindly tell me which path to take——" she began, but the Saxophone interrupted her curtly.

"If you insist on going there, in spite of my advice, take the right-hand path."

"Goodness!" thought Alice, "he *can* be disagreeable when he tries. Maybe the other instruments were right, after all." And without further ado she turned and walked away down the right-hand path.

The path presently became a road, and the road a village street which ended at a square in the centre of the town. The square was thronged with brass instruments of all shapes and sizes, some strolling about in groups, some sitting on benches, others lounging comfortably on the soft grass of the lawns, all listening to spirited strains of music which came from a little circular pavilion, with a roof like a Japanese umbrella, which stood in the middle of the square.

Some of the instruments stared at Alice curiously as she passed, but as they didn't seem unfriendly she was not a bit afraid; and making her way to a point near the pavilion, she found a seat from which she could both see and hear all that went on. She had scarcely sat down, however, when the music came to an end, and the instruments in the pavilion arose and began to pack up their musicians, which, Alice noticed, were dressed, not in tail coats and striped trousers, but in neat blue uniforms trimmed with gold braid.

"Oh, dear!" Alice sighed, "aren't they going to play any more?"

"Not to-day, I'm afraid," said a mellow, bell-like voice close beside her.

Alice was startled. She had not realized that she was speaking aloud, and the answer to her question was unexpected. Turning quickly, she saw seated on the other end of her bench a gleaming, rotund instrument who smiled at her amiably. He consisted of a circular coil of brass tube, about as thick as a pencil at one end and flaring out at the other into a bell as large as a dinner plate. Within the circular coil were several loops of tube connected with three valves, to which were attached levers evidently intended to be operated by the player's fingers; and the smaller end of his tube was fitted with a mouthpiece shaped like a tiny funnel. If all his coils and loops had been straightened out he would have been about twelve feet long, but as it was he would have fitted snugly into a bushel basket.

"You arrived just a bit too late," he said, beaming genially upon Alice. "The concerts end at five o'clock."

"Oh, I'm sorry!" Alice exclaimed. "I should have liked so much to hear the orchestra. It must be a very fine one."

"It isn't an orchestra—it's a military band; but it's a very good band. We're quite proud of it."

"Aren't a band and an orchestra the same thing?" Alice inquired.

"Oh, no," said the instrument. "A band has no strings—no violins or violas or 'cellos—only wind and percussion instruments."

"Which is the best?" Alice asked.

"Well," replied the instrument, "that depends.

The band can play louder than the orchestra, which makes it more effective for concerts in the open air or for military music. But of course it lacks the variety and refinement of the symphony orchestra."

"Which do you play in?"

"Both. But I really do my best work in the orchestra. I think I may say that I am one of its most important members, because I am the only one whose tone blends equally well with the tone of the strings, the wood-wind, or the other brasses."

Alice was duly impressed, and wondered who this very important personage could be.

"Would you mind telling me your name?" she said.

The instrument looked at her in surprise.

"Do you mean to say that you don't know who I am!"

"Why, I'm afraid I'm very ignorant," Alice confessed, "but, you see, I'm not acquainted with all the members of the orchestra yet. I've met the strings and the wood-wind, but I haven't been introduced to the brass instruments, so you must excuse me for not knowing who you are."

"In that case you are not to blame," said the instrument condescendingly, "so I will forgive you this time. I am a horn—sometimes called 'French horn' because my valves were invented by a Frenchman. Before the invention of valves, you know, we horns had our limitations. The only tones that we could play were what are called the 'natural tones' or 'harmonics.' Do you know what 'harmonics' are?"

"Yes," said Alice; "the First Violin showed me how to play them by touching a string so that it vibrated in several sections. But you have no strings, so how can you play harmonics?"

"By causing the column of air in my tube to vibrate in several sections. By regulating the pressure of his lips on the mouthpiece and the force with which he blows into it, the player can produce any harmonic he pleases without using the valves at all."

"Then," said Alice, "what are the valves for?"

"They serve the same purpose as the finger-holes and keys of the wood-wind instruments," the Horn explained. "That is, they alter the length of my tube, so that I can play all the tones of the scale. Without them I can play only the harmonics, which are the notes you hear in bugle calls. Let us suppose that instead of a modern French horn I were an old-fashioned 'natural horn' in the key of F—such a horn as Beethoven composed for. I could play bugle calls and hunting calls in the key of F, but I could not play a complete scale; and if I wanted to play in any other key I would have to lengthen my tube by inserting an extra section called a 'crook.' That would take a lot of time and trouble, so it would be impossible for me to change from one key to another very quickly. But now my crooks, instead of being separate lengths of tubing, are fixed to my body and provided with valves, in such a way that the pressure of the player's fingers can bring them instantly into play, either separately or all together. In this way my pitch can be lowered from one to six half-tones, which makes it possible for me to play a complete chromatic scale—that is, the kind of scale you can play on the piano, using both the white and black keys."

"I'm sure that's a great improvement," said Alice. "It must have been rather dull having to play always in the same key, and only a few notes in that."

"In a way it was," the Horn agreed. "Yet, it's simply marvelous how the old composers, who never dreamed of valves, made their horn parts interesting and beautiful. You should hear the lovely horn passage in Weber's over-ture to 'Der Freischütz.' It was written for four natural horns, but by using two horns in F and two in C the composer was able to command all the tones he needed, just as if the horns had been equipped with valves."

"How many horns are there in the orchestra?" Alice asked.

"Generally there are four. For many of the older compositions only two are needed, but modern works usually call for four, or even more. And nowadays we are kept very busy. Of course, no wind instrument can play as continu-ously as the strings; the strain on the player's lips and lungs is too great. So all considerate composers give us frequent rests. As far as most wind instruments are concerned it's for-tunate that they have to do so, for the listener would grow tired of their penetrating tone if he heard too much of it. But with the horns it's different. We have such a variety of tone qual-ity that one could listen to us almost indefinitely without being bored. Our range of emotional expression is almost as great as that of the strings. We can play nearly as softly as the violins, and much more loudly. We can blare as brazenly as trombones, or coo as gently as

flutes.   Our open tones are clear and noble, and
our 'stopped' ones hushed and mysterious."

"Excuse me," Alice interrupted, "but what
do you mean by 'stopped' tones?"

"To make that clear," said the Horn, "I must
first explain the manner in which the player
holds me, which is rather peculiar. His lips
of course, are pressed against my mouthpiece,
and the fingers of his left hand operate my
valves. My bell then projects backward on his
right side, and he supports my weight by plac-
ing his right hand inside my bell, the opening
of which he can, when he wishes, partially close
by making a cup of his hand. That produces a
subdued veiled sound called a 'stopped' tone."

"I see," said Alice; "it's like putting a mute
on a violin."

"Somewhat," the Horn agreed; "but we have
mutes too."   He held up a queer little object of
brass which, like his mouthpiece, resembled a
funnel, but it was considerably larger than the
mouthpiece and its rim was covered with cork.
"This," he said, "is my mute. It fits into my
bell, and as it closes it more tightly than the
player's hand it subdues the tone still more. If
the player then blows very hard my tone sounds
thin and 'reedy,' somewhat like the English

horn. It is an ominous, threatening tone, and composers often use it to express fear or anger. Listen." He inserted the mute into his bell and suddenly emitted a frightful sound, something between a roar and a bleat. Alice jumped and gave a little cry of alarm.

"Here, Pierre!" said a clear, ringing voice close behind her. "What are you up to, frightening this young lady into fits?"

The Horn smiled, a bit sheepishly.

"Hello, Fred," he said, removing his mute and speaking in his natural voice. "I was just showing the young lady how Grieg has used my muted tone to imitate the snarling of the Trolls in his 'Peer Gynt' music. I didn't mean to frighten her."

"I wasn't frightened—really," said Alice; "only startled. It was so sudden."

"Then we forgive him," said the newcomer, "but he'd better not let it happen again."

"All right," said the Horn, good-humoredly; "I promise to be more careful in the future. And now I suppose I ought to present you to the young lady whom you've so gallantly rescued from danger. Young lady, allow me to present my friend the Trumpet."

The Trumpet bowed. In appearance he differed greatly from the Horn, his tube being only about half as long and coiled into an oblong instead of a circular shape, and his bell was much smaller than the Horn's. The keys which operated his valves were of a different type, and his voice, though higher in pitch than the Horn's, was bolder and had a decidedly metallic quality. He carried himself with a military bearing and spoke with the assurance of one accustomed to give orders.

"I'm sure," thought Alice, "that he must have served in the army."

"I have just been explaining to our young friend," said the Horn, "some of the peculiarities of our family. She takes a very intelligent interest in the subject, and would no doubt be glad to learn something of your own personal characteristics."

"Oh, yes!" said Alice eagerly to the Trumpet. "Please tell me all about yourself."

"I should be happy to oblige you," he said, "but I'm afraid I should bore you by repeating a lot of what Pierre has already told you. So I think he had better continue the story."

"Very well," agreed the Horn. "I accept the responsibility on the condition that you stand by to correct me in case I make any mistakes."

"To go back to the very beginning of the story, the Trumpet was born, so to speak, on the battlefield, while I was born in the forest. The Trumpet was originally a soldier, while I was originally a huntsman."

"Aha!" thought Alice, "I was right about his having been in the army."

"For a long, long time the Trumpet, like myself, had no valves. Therefore he could only play the 'natural' tones of the scale; but now he too has valves which enable him to play all the notes of the chromatic scale. In that respect, you see, our histories are quite similar. But in character, as well as in appearance, we differ greatly. As I have already pointed out, the Trumpet was originally a military instrument, and while he is no longer restricted to martial music, he still retains his old brilliance and boldness—still suggests the dashing warrior. True, he can sing as gently and sweetly as you please—when he wishes to; but when he chooses to open that brazen throat of his and shout with all his might, the very walls tremble. He fairly deafens us at times."

"Couldn't he be muted?" Alice inquired, looking slyly at the Trumpet.

"Oh, yes," said the Horn. "Sometimes he is. Fred, let the young lady hear your voice with the mute."

The Trumpet obligingly produced his mute, which was a sort of hollow cone made of tough cardboard, and inserted it in his bell.

"You would scarcely recognize me now, would you?" he said. His voice had become thin and nasal, with a strong "reedy" quality.

"Now," said the Horn, when the demonstration was concluded, "I must tell you something about the brass section as a whole. It is composed of trumpets, horns, trombones, and a bass tuba. Together, they form a quartet similar to the string quartet and the wood-wind quartet, the trumpets taking the soprano part, the horns the alto, the trombones the tenor, and the tuba the bass. It is only in modern compositions, however, that you will find all of these instruments employed. The older composers, up to the time of Beethoven, never wrote for the tuba —which is a comparatively new instrument— and rarely for trombones. The brass section of their orchestra consisted merely of two trumpets and two horns; but nowadays composers gener-

ally require from two to four trumpets, four or
more horns, three trombones, and one tuba.
With all these instruments they can obtain a
volume of sound that is almost overpowering,
while with the three trombones and tuba they
can reproduce the most sonorous and beautiful
organ effects. But you have not yet met the
Trombone and the Tuba, have you?"

Alice shook her head.

The Horn glanced round the square, through
which a few instruments were still strolling.
Among them was one of rather less complicated
form than his fellows. His tube, which was
fitted with a cup-shaped mouthpiece, extended
straight downward for about three feet, then
doubled back in the opposite direction, and finally curved downward again and ended in a
bell nearly as large as the Horn's. He had
neither crooks nor valves, which gave him an
appearance of dignified simplicity.

The Horn pointed him out to Alice. "There,"
he said, "is a Trombone."

"Why, I recognize him," said Alice. "He
slides in and out like a telescope, doesn't he?"

"He does," said the Horn. "Do you know
why?"

"No, I'm afraid I don't," Alice confessed.

"Then let me explain.   As you know, in order for a wind instrument to play a complete scale it is necessary to alter its length.   In the case of the wood-wind instruments that is done by covering or uncovering holes which are pierced in the tube.   Trumpets and horns achieve the same result by means of crooks controlled by valves.   The trombone, however, has neither finger-holes nor valves.   Instead, it is provided with one long crook, called a 'slide'; and by moving this slide out or in the tube can be lengthened or shortened sufficiently to produce all the tones of the chromatic scale.   It's a very simple arrangement.   Too bad that the same idea could not have been applied to us, instead of all these complicated crooks and valves; but we are coiled up into so many curves and loops that it was impossible.   Most of the trombone's tube, you observe, is straight.   It is bent in only two places, which not only makes the slide arrangement possible, but is chiefly responsible for the remarkable purity and nobility of his tone."

"Is he always so calm and dignified?" Alice inquired, much impressed by the majestic bearing of the Trombone.

"Not always," replied the Horn.   "Occasion-

ally he loses his temper, and when he's angry his
voice is absolutely terrifying. But usually he
is in a mood of noble exaltation, and at times
he's as religious as a monk. A quartet of three
trombones and a bass tuba can play hymns or
chorales with a solemnity that is awe-inspiring.

"What is the Tuba like?" Alice asked.

"You can see for yourself," said the Horn.
"That is he who has just joined the Trombone."

Alice beheld an enormous, clumsy instrument
which waddled beside the erect and austere
Trombone with the gait of an excessively fat
duck. The contrast between the pair was so
comical that Alice could not help laughing.
They reminded her of Jack Sprat and his wife.
Presently a puzzled expression came into her
eyes. What was it about the Tuba that seemed
vaguely familiar? Where had she seen that
mouthpiece, almost as large as a teacup; those
bewildering coils of fat brass tube, and that huge
upturned bell, large enough to swallow her?
Try as she might, she could not quite remember.
Somewhere she had encountered this instrument
before; but it was all very dim and far away and
confusing, and after a moment she dismissed the
question from her mind.

"I do wish I could hear his voice," she said to the Horn. "It must be frightfully deep."

"It is indeed," the Horn assured her. "Next to the Double Bassoon's his voice is the lowest in the orchestra—except his brother's, that is. He has a big brother, you know—the Double Bass Tuba—who can reach the lowest B-flat on the piano. But the brother is so ponderous that he seldom goes out. You will rarely find him at orchestral concerts. At all events, the Bass Tuba's voice is quite low enough and powerful enough for ordinary purposes. His compass extends from the B-flat below Middle C down to the lowest E-flat on the piano, and he sounds like the rumble of distant thunder. There!— you can hear him now."

The Tuba had suddenly been seized with merriment, and his chuckles filled the square with waves of reverberating sound, so low in pitch that Alice was not sure whether she heard it or only felt it, as one sometimes feels the vibration of a passing train.

"Ooh!" she cried, "that's funny! I wish he'd do it again."

But the Tuba had recovered his gravity, and presently passed out of sight, walking arm in arm with his sedate companion, the Trombone.

"Now," said the Horn, "I think you are acquainted with all the members of our interesting family."

"You forget," interposed the Trumpet, "my cousin the Cornet. The Cornet," he explained to Alice, "is a sort of poor relation of mine who, I regret to say, is not often admitted into the best instrumental society."

"Why not?" Alice demanded. "Doesn't he behave properly?"

"He behaves as well as he can," said the Trumpet. "He means well, but the poor fellow is rather lacking in tone. He has neither brilliance nor refinement—and the worst of it is that he looks so much like me that we are sometimes mistaken for one another. But of course no really observant person would be guilty of that error, for he's shorter than I am and a good deal stouter."

Alice asked what he did in the orchestra.

"He very seldom does anything at all," said the Trumpet, "except in inferior orchestras that have no trumpets. Then he sometimes has the presumption to try to take my place. Otherwise he is only permitted to help in producing certain rather vulgar effects, as in Tschaikowsky's 'Italian Caprice,' where two cornets sing a Neapolitan street song. For that sort of thing I must say his tone does well enough. By the bye, are you going to the concert this evening?"

Alice assured him that she would not miss it for anything.

"Quite right," said the Trumpet. "It will be a splendid opportunity for you to see and hear us all in action, for the programme is unusually varied and interesting. May I have the pleasure of escorting you to the hall?"

"Thank you very much," said Alice, rather flattered at receiving an invitation from so distinguished a personage. "I'm afraid, though, I shall have to go alone. You see, I have to visit some other instruments first—the drums and things."

"Oh," said the Trumpet, "you haven't met the percussion instruments yet? Come with me, then—we'll call on them at once. They live at the Battery, sometimes called the 'Kitchen' because it's so full of pots and pans and things. It's just at the end of the village." The Trumpet offered his arm, and Alice, after thanking the genial Horn for his kindness, was led away by her new guide.

CHAPTER VII

ALICE INSPECTS THE ARTILLERY

THE Battery proved to be a large circular building with only a few small windows and a single door. It reminded Alice of the New York Aquarium, which she had visited on several occasions; but this building evidently contained something very different from fish, judging by the extraordinary sounds that issued from it. Indeed, as they drew near, Alice began to fear that the Trumpet had made a mistake and was about to lead her into the midst of a battle or riot. From the interior of the Battery came a deafening uproar of exploding bombs, rumbling cannon, clashing metal, and clanging bells, which, as they approached the entrance, increased to such an alarming extent that Alice involuntarily shrank back and covered her ears with her hands.

"Don't be afraid," the Trumpet shouted reassuringly; "it's only the Artillery at practice. Wait here a moment—I'll soon put a stop to this racket." Stepping inside the doorway, he cried at the top of his voice: " 'Ten-*shun!*" and instantly the noises ceased.

Alice was astonished. "How on earth do you make them mind?" she asked, as the Trumpet reappeared to conduct her into the building.

"It's quite simple," he replied. "I merely give the word of command, and the habit of obedience does the rest. They're good soldiers, you see."

Alice did see, for as she passed through the doorway she beheld an impressive spectacle of order and discipline. In the center of an immense hall, drawn up in military array and standing rigidly at attention, were all the instruments of percussion. There were battalions of kettledrums, companies of bass drums, platoons of snare drums, and squads of miscellaneous instruments, such as cymbals, tambourines, gongs, and triangles.

The Trumpet led Alice to a point near the end of the first rank of instruments, where he halted and again shouted a command:

"Prepare for inspection! Open ranks—march!" and instantly each rear rank fell back two paces, leaving room for Alice and the Trumpet to pass between it and the front rank.

"Now," said the Trumpet, "let us pretend that you are a visiting general inspecting an army. We will walk slowly along the ranks, and as we go I will explain the various units and what they do. These," he said, as he led Alice along the very foremost rank, "are the kettledrums—so called because they look like big copper kettles; now you see why some people call this place the 'Kitchen.' But the kettledrums are also known as *timpani,* which is Italian for drums. They consist, as you see, of a large copper bowl over which is stretched a piece of sheepskin, called a 'head.' The head can be tightened by means of these six set-screws round the rim, so that it gives out a musical tone of definite pitch. That makes the kettledrum the most important and useful of all the percussion instruments, for the others—with a few exceptions which we will discuss later—can only produce noises."

Beside each drum lay a pair of drumsticks with padded heads. Taking up one of these, the Trumpet struck a light blow upon the head of one of the kettledrums, which gave out a low, resonant "boom."

"This one," said the Trumpet, "is tuned to C; and the next one"—striking its neighbor—"is tuned to G, a fourth lower. That is how we generally find them in the classic orchestra; a pair of kettledrums, one tuned to the 'tonic' or keynote, the other tuned to the 'dominant'—the fourth tone below the keynote. For many years the work they had to do was very simple. All that was expected of them was to emphasize the rhythm with single strokes, or else to reinforce the bass by means of a 'roll'—like this": the Trumpet struck the drum very rapidly with two sticks alternately, which caused it to give out a soft, sustained rumble that sounded not unlike a low organ tone.

"Beethoven, however," the Trumpet continued, "discovered that the kettledrums could do more than that. He promoted them to the rank of solo instruments, and wrote many interesting and dramatic passages for them; and ever since his day the kettledrums have been growing in importance. Modern composers often write for three or four, or even more, kettledrums, and they frequently make the drummer tune them to different tones during the performance of a piece."

"That must be hard to do," said Alice.

"It is," the Trumpet agreed. "The kettledrummer must have a very good ear to be able to tune his drums in a new key while the rest of the orchestra is playing in the old one. Now, watch carefully and I'll show you how he does it."

Again he struck the first drum a single blow.

"This one, you remember, is tuned to C. Now suppose we wish to change it to D——" With a quick motion of his wrist he gave each of the set-screws a half-turn to the right, and then, with one ear close to the "head" of the instrument, he tapped it gently with his finger. "It's a little sharp," he said, turning the screws back a little way. "Now I think it's about right." He struck the drum, and it sounded a perfect D.

"How clever of you!" cried Alice, clapping her hands.

"Oh, that's nothing," said the Trumpet modestly. "It isn't very difficult to tune one drum in a quiet place, but to tune three or four while a whole orchestra is playing all around you is quite another matter. If you watch the kettle-drummer the next time you go to a symphony concert you will see a very busy man. And now let us pass on to the next company."

This company was composed of huge cylinders, as big around as a cart wheel and about eighteen inches long, with tightly stretched sheepskin over each end.

"These," said the Trumpet, "are the bass drums. There isn't very much to tell about them. They only make a noise—not a musical sound—and they are used in the orchestra only occasionally, to give rhythmic thumps or to imitate such sounds as thunder or cannon shots. They are usually played with a single stick, but sometimes two kettledrum sticks are used for playing rolls.

"Those little fellows behind the bass drums are snare drums or military drums. They are the same shape, you see, as the bass drums, but much smaller, and across the lower of their two sheepskin 'heads' are stretched several strands of catgut, called 'snares.' When the upper head is struck the snares vibrate against the lower head, producing a peculiar rattling sound. The snare drum is seldom used in symphony orchestras except for the performance of martial music.

"Next we come to the tambourines. They look somewhat like small, flat drums, but they have only one head, and the rim is mounted with a number of small metal disks that jingle agreeably when the tambourine is struck or shaken. It is most often used to lend color to dance music —particularly to Oriental or Spanish dance music.

"The large round plates of brass, just behind the tambourines, are cymbals. They are generally used in pairs, the player holding them by the straps which are fixed to their backs and striking them together. Thus played they give out a deafening metallic clash, very thrilling when heard at the climax of an exciting piece of music. Sometimes a single cymbal is played with a drumstick; and a cymbal roll, played with two kettledrum sticks, is one of the strangest and most mysterious sounds the orchestra can produce.

"There is one instrument, however, that is even more awe-inspiring than the cymbal—the gong. Do you see those great round trays of metal? They are gongs. They are made of bronze, and when struck with a padded drumstick they sound like an enormous, deep-toned bell. They fairly make you shudder.

"These little bars of steel, bent into a three-cornered shape, are triangles. They are played with a small steel rod, and add a delightful silvery tinkle to music of a delicate character. When played *tremolo,* very loudly, they intensify the most brilliant climaxes.

"The castanets, which you see here, consist of a small shell of hard wood loosely attached to a wooden plate with a short handle. By striking the plate against the palm of one hand the player causes the little shell to knock against it with a peculiar hollow click that is quite agreeable when heard in its proper place. Castanets were originally used by Spanish dancers to accompany their performances, but the original castanets were slightly different in form from those now used in the orchestra. They consisted of pairs of shells held together by strings which passed over the performer's forefinger. A pair was held in each hand, and the shells were clapped together by opening and closing the other fingers. In the orchestra the castanets are generally used to lend color to Spanish music."

Alice and the Trumpet had now reached a row of instruments that looked like rather large toy pianos. They had keyboards like that of a piano, but with fewer keys—only four octaves. The Trumpet struck a chord on one of them, and Alice was entranced by its lovely, ethereal tone.

"Oh, how heavenly!" she exclaimed.

"It is indeed," said the Trumpet; "which proves that the instrument is well named. It's called the celesta, and its tone, as you have just observed, is truly celestial."

"What's inside it?" Alice inquired, trying to peep into the case.

"Little bars of steel placed over wooden sound boxes that amplify the tone. The bars are struck by padded hammers, like the hammers of a piano, which are controlled by the keyboard. The celesta, you see, is one of those percussion instruments which, like the kettledrum, produce definite musical tones. Its use in the orchestra is quite varied, but it figures only in comparatively modern compositions.

"Now, *these* instruments," the Trumpet continued, leading Alice to the row next behind the celestas, "also consist of bars of steel; but they have no keyboard, no padded hammers, and no sound boxes. They are played with two sticks, like small kettledrum sticks. with hard knobs, and they sound like tiny bells—from which fact they derive their name, for they are called 'bells.'

"In the next row we find the xylophones. They resemble the bells in form, and are played in the same manner, but instead of bars of steel they have bars of wood, which produce a much less resonant and peculiarly hollow tone. They seldom appear in the orchestra, though they have won great popularity as solo instrument in vaudeville."

Alice and her guide had now arrived at the last rank of instruments—tall racks from which were suspended rows of steel tubes of different lengths.

"These," said the Trumpet, "are the chimes. They are played with a wooden mallet and sound like church bells—only they are generally in better tune. They are often used in music of a solemn or religious character, sometimes singly, sometimes in groups of three or four, sometimes an entire octave.

"And now you have met all the members of the orchestra—so let us go, or we shall be late for the concert."

"Don't they get tired standing still for such a long time?" Alice asked the Trumpet as they passed the ranks of rigid instruments on their way to the door.

"They don't mind," he replied. "As I said before, they are good soldiers. However, we may as well give them a rest"—and just as he was leaving the building he shouted: "As you were!" whereupon the rattling and banging and clashing broke out again as furiously as before. As Alice and the Trumpet left the Battery farther and farther behind them the noise grew gradually fainter, until at last it was lost in the distance.

CHAPTER VIII

A CONCERT IN ORCHESTRALIA

THE walk back to Fiddladelphia, where the concert was to take place, seemed to Alice to take almost no time at all. The Trumpet knew a short cut across the fields, and as they proceeded he entertained Alice with anecdotes of his career so amusing that she was sorry when they arrived at the Conservatory and the stories came to an end. As they entered the great marble hall crowds of instruments of all kinds—string, wood-wind, brass, and percussion—were arriving and flocking into the auditorium; but standing aside from the throng, alone and neglected, was a very large and beautiful instrument which Alice had not seen before. It was nearly six feet tall, triangular in shape, and made of beautiful cream-colored wood lavishly ornamented with gold. Across its triangular frame from top to bottom ran a large number of strings, placed about three quarters of an inch apart, and from the rear of the pedestal on which it stood projected seven pedals like the pedals of a piano.

Alice knew without being told that it must be a harp, for she had seen many pictures of harps of different kinds, and while this one was much larger than she had ever imagined a harp could be she recognized it for a member of that ancient and noble family.

Observing Alice's gaze fixed on the Harp, the Trumpet said: "Evidently there is one member of our family whom you have not met, after all; shall I present him?"

"Oh, please do," said Alice. "But first tell me something about him. Why does he seem so lonely?"

"Well, you see, he's not a regular member of the orchestra. He plays with us only occasionally, mostly in rather modern compositions, so he never has a chance to get really well acquainted with the rest of us. That's why he holds himself somewhat aloof."

"But surely he must have some friends in the village," said Alice. "Does he live in Fiddladelphia?"

"No," said the Trumpet; "and, strange as it may seem, nobody knows exactly where he does live. You see, he's a stringed instrument, of course—that's plain as day, because he has lots of strings—forty-six of them; but he's certainly not a fiddle, because he's not played with a bow. Therefore he doesn't belong in Fiddladelphia. He's not a wind instrument either, so he doesn't belong in Panopolis or Brassydale, and he's not a percussion instrument, so his place is not in the 'Kitchen.' He's such a modest sort of chap and so seldom talks about himself that we've never found out where his home is, but we suspect that it's out in the country, with the pianos."

"Why," said Alice, "are there pianos in Orchestralia too?"

"Only a few. They are not really orchestral instruments, but occasionally they are called on to help us out—to-night, as it happens, we shall have the assistance of two of them."

"Oh, good!" Alice exclaimed. "I'm so glad

they do have pianos in orchestras sometimes; perhaps I can play in an orchestra some day!"

"There's no reason why you shouldn't—if you practise hard," said the Trumpet, encouragingly. "But let me tell you a little more about the Harp. As I said, he has forty-six strings, which give him a compass of a little more than six octaves—a range almost as great as that of the piano; but in most respects, he differs widely from the piano and is much more limited as to the kinds of music he can play. In a way, he is somewhat like a piano with the black keys missing, for his strings are tuned to what we call the *diatonic* scale—that is, the scale without any accidental sharps or flats—and, while each string can be sharpened a half tone or a whole tone by means of the pedals, it can't be done rapidly enough to enable him to play *chromatic* passages—which, as you know, means successions of half tones. So what he usually does is to play broken chords, which are called *arpeggios,* a term derived from *arpa,* the Italian word for harp. Those he can play in any key—provided you give him time to change his pedals. He also has a very brilliant and thrilling trick called the *glissando,* which no other instrument can imitate. It is done by running the finger rapidly up and down the strings, which produces a perfect cascade of lovely tones. The effect is simply indescribable; once you have heard it you will never forget it. And now let us go and speak to the Harp, for it's nearly time to take our seats."

Alice found the Harp a most agreeable instrument, with his gentle, courteous manners and mellow, resonant voice, and when the Trumpet presently departed to take his place on the stage she accepted with pleasure the Harp's offer to sit beside her during the first part of the programme (he had nothing to play until the last number) and to explain anything she might find puzzling.

Their seats were in a box, quite near the stage, from which point Alice had an excellent view of the entire orchestra, all of whose members she now knew by sight and by name—all, that is, except one, for presently there emerged from behind the scenes an instrument which appeared to be nothing more than a slender white stick about eighteen inches long.

"Who is that?" Alice asked in a whisper.

"Why, that," replied the Harp, "is Mr. Baton."

"What a queer-looking instrument!" said Alice. "What sort of sound does he make?"

"He doesn't make any sound at all—only motions. You see, he's the conductor."

Mr. Baton, who in the meantime had crossed the stage to the little raised platform in the center, bowed in acknowledgment of the applause which greeted his appearance and then sprang lightly into the waiting hand of the very distinguished-looking dummy which stood upon the platform—and instantly he seemed to lose his individuality and become merely a slender white stick which the distinguished-looking dummy appeared to do with as it pleased. The first thing it did was to rap with the stick upon the desk which held its music, whereupon the audience all stopped talking and fidgeting and rustling their programmes. Then it made a sign to the First 'Cello, who began to play, all alone, a phrase which began on his lowest string and soared upward to a note far up on his highest string. It reminded Alice of a mountain peak rising majestically out of the valley; indeed, throughout the entire introduction, which was played by five 'cellos, accompanied only by the basses, she had but to close her eyes to imagine herself in some high Alpine valley, surrounded by snow-covered peaks—and that was strange, for Alice had never seen the Alps; but there was something about the music that seemed to tell her what they were like.

Presently, through the song of the 'cellos was heard the muttering of distant thunder. Alice knew, of course, that it came from the kettle-drum, but it sounded so much like real thunder that she couldn't help wishing that she had brought her umbrella. After a moment there was another peal of thunder, nearer now; and then, as the sunny melody in the 'cellos was gradually blotted out by the gathering clouds, the storm began. At first there was only the uneasy stirring of the wind in the violins and a few scattered drops of rain in the wood-winds; but soon the wind increased in violence, the peals of thunder grew louder, and the tempest broke in all its fury, with lightning flashing and rain pouring in torrents.

The storm spent its fury at last, and as the clouds rolled away over the mountains Alice heard the song of a bird (sung by the silvery flute) rejoicing because the sunshine had come back again. Then came the sound of a shepherd's pipe—Alice recognized her melancholy friend, the English Horn—whose plaintive notes were repeated by the echo from across the valley. The scene was now a lovely, tranquil one of green pastures and grazing flocks of sheep over which the shepherd kept watch while he played upon his pipe. All was as calm and peaceful as could be, and nobody seemed to have anything very pressing to do—except the First Flute. He was kept extremely busy representing both the echo and the bird, which seemed to be inspired by the shepherd's pipe to sing the most elaborate and difficult songs it could think of.

Suddenly the shepherd's piping and the bird's song were interrupted by a trumpet call, answered by a fanfare of hunting horns, and out of the forest came a splendid procession of soldiers and huntsmen, all clad in green and armed with spears and swords and cross-bows. They passed down the valley to the tune of a gay, triumphant march, in which the entire orchestra joined; then, just as they had all assembled in an open space, as if to hold some kind of celebration, the music rose to a tremendous climax and came to an end; and with the final chord the scene vanished, and Alice saw only the stage with its array of instruments, and Mr. Baton, the conductor, bowing his thanks for the applause.

Alice was amazed to find how music seemed to tell her stories and make her see pictures—"moving pictures," only they were better, because the "movies" were merely black and white, while these were full of beautiful, brilliant colors.

"Did you like that number?" the Harp inquired.

"Oh, it was simply marvelous!" Alice exclaimed. "What is the name of it?"

"Tell me first," said the Harp, "what you think it meant—what it seemed to express."

"Why," said Alice, enthusiastically, "it was all about mountains and a storm and a shepherd playing on his pipe and soldiers with bows and arrows!"

"What makes you think they had bows and arrows?" said the Harp. "Why not guns?"

"Oh, no," said Alice, positively, "the music sounded like bows and arrows—not like guns at all."

"Well," said the Harp, laughing, "you're quite right; for that piece was the overture to 'William Tell,' which, as you may know, is an

opera by Rossini. Its scene is laid in Switzer-
land, about five hundred years ago, and it tells
the story of a patriot who freed his country from
a foreign tyrant."

"Oh, yes—I know," cried Alice. "William
Tell shot an apple off his little boy's head with
his bow and arrow!"

"Exactly," said the Harp. "But we mustn't
talk any more now, for the next piece is about
to begin. It's the second movement from
Beethoven's Sixth Symphony, and it's called
'The Scene by the Brook.' Listen attentively
and you'll hear the murmuring of the water and
the singing of birds, and all the lovely sounds
of nature on a summer day."

As the orchestra began to play again Alice
gave a little start of surprise. What was that
gentle, flowing, rippling melody that the strings
were singing, and why did it seem so familiar
to her? All at once she remembered: it was
the song of the brook which she had heard and
learned by heart on her way from Panopolis to
Brassydale. But now it was fuller and richer,
as if the brook had joined other brooks and become almost a river. On and on it flowed,
calmly and smoothly, never hurrying, constantly
changing and yet always the same, while the

sound of the breeze among the rushes and the songs of birds in the trees added richness and variety to the ever-changing harmonies. Just before the end a nightingale began to sing—it was really the flute, of course—and the brook seemed to stop flowing, as if to listen. A quail and a cuckoo—really the oboe and clarinet—answered the nightingale, and then gradually darkness fell and all was silent.

The next number on the programme proved to be of quite a different kind—gay and jolly and full of excellent musical jokes. It was called "The Carnival of the Animals," and the Harp told Alice that, though it had been written by Saint-Saëns, the famous French composer, many years ago, he had permitted it to be played only two or three times during his life, so that very few people had ever heard it. It was really a suite, or series, of fourteen short pieces, each one representing some member of the animal kingdom. The first was called the "Royal March of the Lion," and Alice was astonished to find how well pianos—there were two of them in the orchestra for this number—could imitate the roaring of the King of Beasts.

The next movement was called "Hens and Roosters," and from the way the pianos and the violins and violas and the clarinet cackled and crowed one would have thought that they had all grown feathers and turned into barnyard fowls. In the third movement the two pianos alone gave a wonderful imitation of the fleet-footed wild asses running at furious speed over the plains. Then came "Turtles," represented by the strings playing a very fast tune very slowly, which suggested most amusingly the motions of those clumsy creatures.

The title of the next movement was "Elephants," and Alice remembered that the First Violin had told her that in this piece the basses gave an imitation of elephants dancing a minuet. Sure enough, they did, and so well that although Alice had never seen elephants dance a minuet she could quite well imagine them doing it, with their ears and trunks waving solemnly, and trying very hard to be graceful. The effect was so funny that all the audience laughed aloud.

The next piece was a realistic imitation by the pianos of two kangaroos hopping about on their enormous hind legs; and then came one called "The Aquarium," in which the Flute, the Celesta, and the muted strings represented the cool, transparent water, through which, like lazy, many-hued fish, swam graceful piano *arpeggios.*

"Persons with Long Ears" was the title o the next movement, and Alice wondered whethe they were rabbits or donkeys. She soon foun out, for the violins began to bray so plaintivel that she was sorry she hadn't any carrots t offer them. They very soon ceased complain ing, however, and the pianos began to play beau tiful soft chords which made one think of a forest at twilight; and presently, from very fal away—it was the Clarinet, the Harp explained, playing behind the scenes—came the notes of a cuckoo. Alice knew it was a cuckoo because it sounded like the one in the tall clock at home, except that it was much softer and more musical.

In the movement which followed, called "The Bird House," all the little twittering, chirping birds in the world seemed to be gathered to- gether. It was difficult to believe that they were really only the flute, pianos, and stringed instruments of the orchestra. The next piece puzzled Alice a little, for it was called "Pian- ists," and she didn't quite see why they should be included among the birds and beasts; but she couldn't help laughing at the imitation of a young pianist practising scales and exercises, for it sounded so much like her own early at- tempts to master the difficulties of Czerny. The next movement was called "Fossils," and the Harp had to explain that fossils were the remains of prehistoric animals that had been dead thousands of years—one saw them in natural history museums, you know. They were represented by some very old tunes which the composer apparently thought had been heard often enough and ought to be kept in museums too. After that came a lovely serene movement called "The Swan," in which the pianos played a soft, rippling accompaniment while a beautiful melody in the 'cello glided about with all the stately grace of that most graceful water-fowl. The final movement, which came next, brought all the animals together in a sort of general jollification, and the suite ended with the merry braying of the "persons with long ears."

Only one more number remained to be played, and that, the programme stated, was the "Waltz of the Flowers," by Tschaikowsky. Alice didn't dare try to pronounce the composer's name—it seemed to be full of letters that didn't match—and the Harp wasn't there to help her, for he had a part to play in this piece and had gone to take his place on the stage. But she felt sure that the music would be less forbidding than the strange collection of consonants in the composer's name—and it was. It began with an introduction in which the swaying waltz theme was announced by the wood-wind and horns while the Harp played great sweeping *arpeggios*. Then the sound of the wind instrument died away, leaving the Harp to execute a brilliant *cadenza,* or solo passage, that surged upward, higher and higher, like waves on a beach and then subsided gradually, to end in a series of rippling chords. The waltz rhythm then began again with plucked chords in the lower stringed instruments, and presently the horns again took up the lilting, swinging theme, which the Clarinet embroidered now and then with a delicate tracery of notes. It seemed to Alice as if she were in an enchanted garden, surrounded by vast numbers of flowers of every kind and color, all swaying and nodding and bowing in time with the music. More and more exciting grew the dance; new themes appeared, more enchanting than the first; new instruments added their voices to the chorus; more and more dizzying became the motions of the swaying blossoms. Then, suddenly, with a deafening crash, the music ceased.

Alice felt quite bewildered. She rubbed her

yes and stared at the stage. Something appeared to be wrong with the orchestra, though he was not sure what it was. Then she noticed that Mr. Baton was not bowing his acknowledgment of the applause as usual. Instead, he was lying on the music desk, and the dummy conductor was bowing for him. But *was* it a dummy conductor? It certainly looked amazingly like a real live human being. Had it suddenly come to life? Why, all the dummies had come to life—they were all getting up and leaving the stage, and they were carrying their instruments, which no longer showed any signs of life. What on earth could have happened?

Just then a voice behind her said, "Come along, Alice. The concert's over and we mustn't miss our train."

Alice turned and, to her astonishment, saw her mother beckoning to her. Without realizing where she was going she followed her mother out of the hall and into a cab. As they drove through the busy streets to the station she tried to untangle the confused thoughts that filled her mind. Was she still in Orchestralia —had she ever been there? Had she really talked with fiddles and walked with trumpets

and had tea with oboes?   Well, at any rate, she
had had a wonderful time, and had learned a
tremendous lot about the orchestra.

"The only thing I'm quite sure of," she said
to herself, "is that it was *not* a dream."

THE END

APPENDIX

The Orchestra

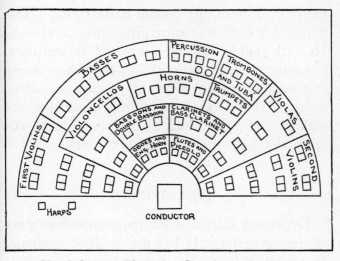

Usual Seating Plan of a Symphony Orchestra

The modern symphony orchestra consists of four groups or "sections" of instruments—the "strings," the "wood-winds," the "brasses," and the instruments of percussion, sometimes called "the battery." Each of these groups (except the "battery"), is composed of four "parts," or "voices," similar to the four voices of a vocal quartet. These three quartets form the basis of the orchestra, to which have been added at various times a number of auxiliary instruments, such as the harp, the piccolo, the English horn, the bass clarinet, the double bassoon, etc. The percussion section is quite differently composed. Its only regular members are the kettledrums, but some modern compositions require as many as a dozen different kinds of percussion instruments. Most of these are merely musical noise-makers, but a few, such as the kettledrums, celesta, and bells, produce definite tones.

THE STRINGS

The string section is the most important part of the orchestra. It has the greatest compass, or range of tones, the greatest range of emotional expression, the greatest facility of execution, and the greatest dynamic range—that is, it can produce the widest variety of loudness and softness. The stringed instruments can also be played more continuously than any others without fatiguing the performers (players of wind instruments must have frequent rests in order

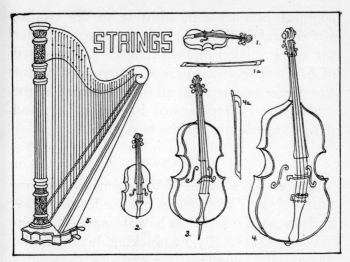

1. Violin. 1a. Violin Bow. 2. Viola. 3. Violoncello.
4. Bass Viol. 4a. Bass Viol Bow. 5. Harp.

to recover their breath and relax the muscles of their lips), and the tone of the stringed instruments is more agreeable to listen to steadily than that of the other instruments.

In the description of the string quartet in Chapter III the first violin was said to represent the soprano, the second violin the alto, the viola the tenor, and the 'cello the bass of the vocal quartet. This comparison must be altered slightly to fit the orchestral string quartet, which contains bass viols in addition to the violins, violas, and 'cellos. Let us therefore consider the string section of the orchestra as composed of first and second sopranos, represented by the first and second violins; altos, represented by the violas; tenors, represented by the 'cellos; and basses, represented by the bass viols.

THE VIOLIN

The violin, soprano of the string section, has four strings. The strings are made to vibrate by drawing across them a bow strung with horse-hair, or, occasionally, by plucking them with the finger. By "stopping," or pressing, the strings against the fingerboard with the fingers of the left hand all the tones of the chromatic scale, within the range of the instrument, may be produced. The violin is essentialy a melodic in-strument—that is, it is best suited to music of a singing type and consisting of only one voice or part. It is possible, however, to play two-part music on the violin (this is called "double-stopping"), and to play chords of two, three, or four tones. "Harmonics" are produced by touching the string lightly with the finger in such a manner that the string vibrates in two or more equal segments; their tone is very delicate and ethereal. The mute, or *sordino,* a little clamp of wood or metal, when placed upon the bridge makes the tone of the violin softer, more veiled and mysterious. The violins of the orchestra are divided into two sections—first violins and second violins. The instruments themselves are exactly alike, but the work they do is different, the first violins generally playing the "tune," or principal melody, while the seconds help to fill in the harmony. Sometimes the seconds play the tune with the firsts, but an octave lower.

THE VIOLA

The viola, alto of the string section, is almost exactly like the violin except that it is a little larger in size, a little lower in pitch, and much more sombre and melancholy in tone quality. In the orchestra it generally serves to fill in the harmony, though it is often given the solo part when the melody is a sad or gloomy one. Like the violin it can produce harmonics and can be muted.

THE VIOLONCELLO

The violoncello, tenor of the string section, is really a small double-bass, or *violone.* It is very much larger than the viola, and is held between the player's knees. It is an octave lower in pitch than the viola, and much fuller, richer, and more powerful in tone, but it is not so melancholy. Indeed, its highest string is particularly brilliant. Its chief duty in the orchestra is to supply either the tenor part of the harmony or the bass part (in that case the bass viols often play the same part an octave lower), but it is also very frequently given the solo, or principal melody. It is played in very much the same manner as the violin and viola, though the fingering is different, owing to its longer strings. It can produce the same effects of harmonics, *pizzicato,* etc., and also uses the mute.

THE BASS VIOL

The bass viol (usually called "double-bass," or simply "bass") is the lowest in pitch of the stringed instruments. It corresponds to the bass voice of the vocal quartet. It is an enormous, clumsy-looking instrument, twice as large as the 'cello, and its range is nearly an octave lower. It is played in nearly the same manner as the 'cello, but the player is obliged to stand in order to reach its lofty neck. Rapid passages, such as may be played with comparative ease on the other stringed instruments, are very difficult on the bass, owing to the great length and thickness of its strings, and its pitch is so low that it is seldom used for melodic work. As a rule its duty is to play the bass part of the harmony, either alone or aided by the 'cellos (an octave higher) or the other bass instruments. Harmonics, *pizzicato,* etc., are possible on the bass, and the mute is sometimes used.

THE HARP

Although the harp is, of course, a stringed instrument (its tone resulting from the vibration of strings), it has nothing in common with the other strings and does not properly belong to their section. Indeed, it rarely appears in the orchestra at all except for the performance of comparatively modern works. It has forty-six strings, tuned to the scale of C-flat but so arranged that by means of pedals their pitch can be altered, thus enabling the harp to play in any key. Its usual function in the orchestra is to play accompaniments in broken chords, or *arpeggios,* but it sometimes has a solo passage, such as a *cadenza* or *glissando.* Harmonics on the harp are very pure and delicate. The range of the harp is almost as great as that of the piano —six and a half octaves.

THE WOOD-WIND

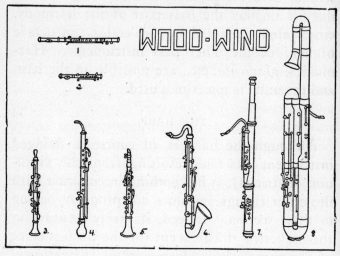

1. Flute. 2. Piccolo. 3. Oboe. 4. English Horn.
5. Clarinet. 6. Bass Clarinet. 7. Bassoon.
8. Double-Bassoon.

The wood-wind section of the orchestra is composed, normally, of two flutes, two oboes, two clarinets, and two bassoons. Modern compositions, however, often require three or four of each, as well as a piccolo, an English horn, a bass clarinet, and a double-bassoon. Still other instruments, such as the bass flute, the oboe d'amore, the E-flat clarinet, and the basset horn, occasionally appear among the wood-wind instruments, but their use is so rare that they need not be considered here. The functions of the wood-wind choir are quite different from those of the strings. They play much less continuously, and more often separately, as solo instruments, their quality of tone being so peculiar and so penetrating that they have no difficulty in making themselves heard above the entire body of strings. Their characteristic *timbres,* or tone qualities, all of which are entirely different from each other, form the principal source of orchestral tone color.

THE FLUTE

The flute is the soprano of the wood-wind section. It is a cylindrical tube, formerly made of wood, but nowadays generally of silver. Its tone is produced by blowing across an opening near the upper, or left-hand, end, which causes the column of air enclosed within its tube to vibrate. The pitch is varied by opening or closing holes in the lower part of the tube and by varying the force of the breath, which shortens or lengthens the vibrating column of air. The tone quality of the flute is pure and delicate, soft and gentle in the lower register, clear and brilliant in the upper. It is generally used as a solo instrument in the orchestra.

THE PICCOLO

The piccolo is exactly like the flute, but is only half as long, and is therefore an octave higher in pitch. Its tone is very brilliant and penetrating—often shrill. It is generally used to brighten the tone color in brilliant passages.

THE OBOE

The oboe, alto of the wood-wind section, is a double-reed instrument—that is, its air column is set in vibration by blowing into a double reed attached to its mouthpiece. This fact, together with the conical shape of its tube, accounts for its peculiarly penetrating, "reedy" quality of tone. Its pitch is varied in the same manner as that of the flute. It is employed chiefly as a solo instrument, and has a great variety of expression, though it is particularly effective in music of a pastoral nature. It "gives the A" to the other instruments of the orchestra—that is, the other instruments tune to it—as its own fundamental pitch can be altered only very slightly.

THE ENGLISH HORN

The English horn is not a horn, but a tenor oboe. It is a double-reed instrument, with a conical tube, but is longer than the oboe and a fifth lower in pitch. Its tone is rich and sombre, very effective for melodies of a melancholy character.

THE CLARINET

The clarinet, tenor of the wood-wind choir, resembles the oboe in appearance, but differs from it materially in mechanism and tone quality. Its tube is cylindrical instead of conical, it is played with a single reed instead of a double one, and its tone is rounder, fuller, and less "reedy" than that of the oboe. Its great range —nearly four octaves—its beautiful, romantic quality of tone, and its facility of execution render it the most useful of all the wood-wind instruments. It is used as a solo instrument for all kinds of music, from slow, tender melodies to the most rapid and brilliant passages.

THE BASS CLARINET

The bass clarinet is twice as long as the clarinet and sounds an octave lower. Its tone is very rich and melancholy, particularly in the lower register. It is a very effective solo instrument for melodies of a tragic or ominous character.

THE BASSOON

The bassoon, bass instrument of the regular wood-wind quartet, has a double reed and a conical tube about eight feet long, which is doubled up to make it less cumbersome to handle. Its tone is very reedy, and may be solemn and dignified or grotesquely comic, according to the character of the music allotted to it. The bassoon is extensively used both as a solo instrument and in combination with others as a harmonic "filler-in." In the latter case it usually provides or reinforces the bass.

THE DOUBLE-BASSOON

The double-bassoon resembles the bassoon in general form and quality of tone, but is twice as long and sounds an octave lower. It is seldom employed as a solo instrument, its duty being usually to reinforce the lowest bass notes of the harmony.

THE BRASSES

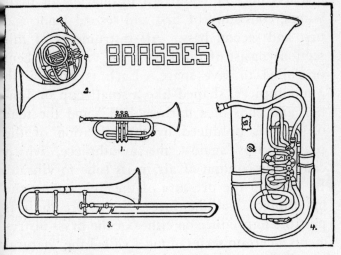

1. Trumpet. 2. Horn. 3. Trombone. 4. Tuba.

The brass section is the most powerful of the orchestra. It can play more loudly than all the other instruments combined, but it cannot play as softly as the strings or wood-wind. It consists, like the other sections, of four types of instruments corresponding roughly to the four voices of the vocal quartet, but the entire section is less frequently employed as a whole, four-part harmony in the brasses being more often furnished by the quartet of horns or by the three trombones and tuba. These two subsidiary quartets may be compared to quartets of male voices, consisting of first and second tenor and first and second bass. All instruments of this section consist of tubes of brass, variously bent or coiled to save space. Each is fitted with a mouthpiece, shaped like a small cup or funnel, and ends in a flaring "bell," and the tone of each is produced by the vibration of the player's lips against the mouthpiece, which causes the column of air in its tube to vibrate. By varying the pressure of the lips against the mouthpiece and the force of the breath it is possible to produce on either of the brass instruments a certain series of tones called the "natural tones" (military bugle calls employ only the lower "natural tones" of the bugle or trumpet), but no brass instrument can play a complete scale unless it is provided with some mechanism for altering the length of its tube. Trumpets, horns, and tubas are therefore equipped with "valves," and trombones with "slides," which enable the player to produce all the notes of the scale by changing the length of his instrument at will.

THE TRUMPET

The range of the trumpet corresponds to that of the soprano voice, but there the resemblance ends, for the trumpet is the most masculine of instruments. It is used in the orchestra chiefly for music of a bold or martial character.

THE HORN

The horn, which occupies a relative position in the brass section corresponding to that of the alto in the vocal quartet, actually has a range about equivalent to that of the tenor voice. It is the most important of all the brass instruments, as its beautiful, mellow quality of tone blends equally well with strings, wood-wind, or other brasses. It is frequently employed as a solo instrument for music of all kinds, gay or sad, brilliant or romantic, and the four horns are often used as a separate quartet or in combination with the wood-wind.

THE TROMBONE

The tenor instrument of the brass section is the tenor trombone. There are usually three of them in the orchestra, though the third is sometimes replaced by a bass trombone, which is a little lower in pitch. Together with the tuba they form a brass quartet of great sonority and majestic dignity, often used for music of a solemn or religious type. The trombone is also very effective as a solo instrument.

THE TUBA

The tuba has the lowest range of any orchestral instrument except the double-bassoon. It provides the bass for the brass section, and is even used occasionally as a solo instrument, chiefly for comic effect, for its pitch is so low and its tone so powerful that its sound is grotesque when heard alone.

THE PERCUSSION INSTRUMENTS

The "battery" of the orchestra in early days consisted only of a pair of kettledrums, whose duty was merely to emphasize the rhythm with resonant thumps or to reinforce the bass of a chord with a "roll." Composers soon discovered, however, that various kinds of "noises," judiciously employed, enhanced the effect of their compositions. The result is that nowadays almost anything that makes a noise is likely to be found at one time or another in the percussion section of an orchestra. As it would be impossible to describe them all here, we shall consider only those which are employed most frequently.

THE KETTLEDRUMS

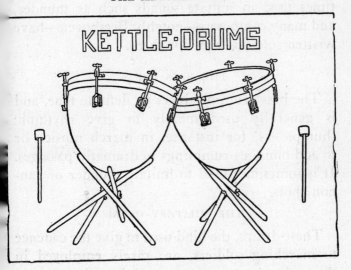

Kettledrums are the most important percussion instruments, and are used in almost all compositions for orchestra. They produce definite musical tones, and must be tuned by the performer, often during the performance of a piece. They are most often used in pairs, one tuned to the key-note, the other to the dominant, though modern compositions sometimes call for as many as six kettledrums. Their function is generally to emphasize the rhythm or to play "rolls," which are very exciting in *fortissimo* and mysterious in *pianissimo;* but they are sometimes used to imitate sounds such as thunder, and many composers—notably Beethoven—have written solo passages for them.

THE BASS DRUM

The bass drum produces no definite tone, and is generally used merely to give rhythmic thumps—as, for instance, in march music—or to add ominous rumblings to dramatic passages. It is sometimes used to imitate thunder or cannon shots.

THE MILITARY DRUM

These drums, the kind used to give the cadence to marching soldiers, are rarely employed in the orchestra except for martial music.

THE TAMBOURINE

The tambourine is used in the orchestra principally for Spanish or Oriental music.

THE CYMBALS

The metallic clash of the cymbals, when struck together, is used to heighten the effect of an exciting climax. They are often used in combination with the bass drum, and a single cymbal is sometimes played with kettledrum sticks.

THE GONG

The gong, used for religious ceremonies by the Chinese, is generally employed in the orchestra for music of a tragic character, its deep, reverberating tone being sinister and terrifying.

THE TRIANGLE

The triangle produces a pleasant, tinkling sound of no definite pitch, somewhat like that of a very small bell. It is delightful in music of a dainty, delicate character, and thrilling when played *fortissimo* in a brilliant climax.

THE CASTANETS

The castanets are seldom used except to mark the rhythm of Spanish dance music.

THE CELESTA

The celesta consists of a set of metal bars of definite pitch, placed over amplifiers and played by hammers controlled by a piano keyboard. Its tone is remarkably pure and bell-like, but not very strong. It is used only in delicate, ethereal passages, generally as a solo instrument.

THE BELLS

The bells also consist of a series of metal bars, but they have no amplifiers, and are played with two hammers held in the hands. Their tone is much stronger and more brilliant than that of the celesta.

THE XYLOPHONE

In form and manner of execution the xylophone resembles the bells, but its bars are of wood and its tone is hollow and not very resonant. It is used in he orchestra only for special effects.

THE CHIMES

These long tubes of steel, of definite pitch, are used to represent church bells, whose sound they imitate admirably.

THE ORCHESTRA AND ITS BUILDERS

In certain cities of the Old World stand great cathedrals famed for their size and their majestic beauty. They are very old, and they will grow much older before they tumble down, for they were well and carefully built—so carefully that some of them took hundreds of years in the building. Generation after generation contributed its portion to the growing mass of stone, one adding a chapel, another a bay, until in the course of time the edifice stood complete, with its lofty arches and soaring spires, a thing of perfect beauty. Just so has the orchestra, which to-day rejoices our ears as the old cathedral rejoices our eyes, been slowly and carefully built up from the humblest foundations. For three hundred years it has been gradually growing and expanding as successive generations of musical builders have added their stones to the structure—and even now it is not complete. Indeed, it probably never will be, for new music, requiring new means of expression, is constantly being written, and consequently new instruments are constantly being added to the orchestra.

In the 16th Century, when Elizabeth was Queen of England and a poet named Shakespeare was beginning to write plays, when America was still the happy hunting ground of the Indians, and the Pilgrims had not yet landed at Plymouth Rock, the foundations of the orchestra were being laid. So humble were those foundations that they have since been almost entirely forgotten. One or two of the original stones are still recognizable—the trumpets and hautboys (oboes), for instance, though time has wrought great changes in them. As for the others—the lutes, the lyres, the viols, the regals —they have disappeared, obscured by the structure that has been built upon them.

In those early days an orchestra was a very indefinite and variable affair. It consisted merely of whatever instruments of any kind a composer could scrape together for a performance of his works, and the part each instrument was to play was usually left almost entirely to the taste and ingenuity of its player. It is rather hard to understand how such an orchestra ever succeeded in producing anything resembling music, but apparently it did, for the popularity of orchestral music steadily increased, and, of course, the orchestras consequently improved, both in quantity and quality. Gradually the instruments of the viol family came to be regarded as the backbone of the orchestra, and, as the violin, the violoncello, and the bass viol were perfected, the older *viola da braccio, viola d'amore,* and *viola da gamba* gave way to them. The harpsichord replaced the lutes and lyres; the flute, oboe, bassoon, horn, and trumpet usurped the places formerly held, rather precariously, by the *flûte à bec,* flageolet, recorder, clarion, and other inferior instruments.

It was not until the time of Haydn, however, that the orchestra became definitely what it is to-day: a balanced choir of three different families of instruments—strings, wood-wind and brasses—with various percussion instruments added as occasion requires. Haydn may be said to have completed the essential structure of the orchestra; the builders since his time have merely enlarged and beautified it by adding a bay or chapel here, a spire or belfry there. Let us see what manner of man he was, how he lived, and what he did for music and the orchestra.

HAYDN

Franz Josef Haydn was born in 1732 at Rohrau, a small village in Austria. His father was a wheelwright, who loved music but knew nothing about it. It was a cousin, named Frankh, who discovered little Josef's talent and took him, at the age of six, to become a pupil in his school at Hainburg. There the youngster learned to sing and to play the violin and harpsichord. His master was very strict, and gave him, as Haydn afterward declared, "more floggings than food." Nevertheless, he seems to have had a very good time, and he certainly made rapid progress in his studies. Two years later he became a choir boy at St. Stephen's, in Vienna, where his education was continued. Here, he was seized with the desire to compose music, and, as his course of studies did not include instruction in composition, he set to work to master the difficult art unaided, scribbling music on every blank sheet of paper he could lay his hands on.

Although he was a diligent student, Haydn was a "regular fellow," always ready to join his comrades in games and pranks. His fondness for mischief, indeed, was the cause of his leaving St. Stephen's sooner than he expected, for when he was sixteen years old he cut off the pigtail of one of his schoolmates, which resulted in his expulsion from the school. He was thus thrown upon the world, without money or friends; but somehow or other he managed to earn a frugal living and continue his study of composition, devouring all the textbooks on the subject he could find and poring over the compositions of Emmanuel Bach, whom he took for his model. In the course of the next few years he gradually became known as a young musician of unusual ability, but he was nearly thirty years old before his great opportunity presented itself. In 1761 he was engaged as chapelmaster, or conductor, at the palace of Prince Esterhazy, member of a noble Hungarian family which for generations had been devoted to music and had maintained its own private orchestra.

Haydn remained in the service of the Esterhazy family all the rest of his life, devoting his time to conducting and composing. Thanks to the wealth and generosity of his patron he was able to experiment to his heart's content with a small but capable orchestra, and to learn by experience the best instruments to employ and the best ways to use and combine them. The orchestra developed by him consisted of a small body of strings (not more than thirty in all) two flutes, two oboes, two bassoons, two natural horns, two natural trumpets, and kettle-drums.

Haydn also perfected, if he did not invent, the symphonic form of composition, and composed more than a hundred and fifty symphonies, in addition to a vast number of other works, nearly all remarkable for their gayety, as well as for their beauty of form. He has been called "the father of the symphony," but his friends called him "Papa Haydn," to show their affection for him, for he was a kind and courteous gentleman, beloved by all who knew him. He died in 1809, at the age of seventy-seven.

MOZART

The next of the great builders of the orchestra was Wolfgang Amadeus Mozart, who was born at Salzburg, Austria, in 1756, when Haydn was a struggling young artist of twenty-four. His origin, his talents, his career, were very different from those of Haydn. Mozart's father was himself an excellent musician, who was able to give his extraordinary son—and daughter (for Wolfgang had a sister, Marianne, who was hardly less gifted than himself)—the best training, and to help them in many ways along the road to success and fame. Mozart was the most wonderful of all wonder-children. At the age of three he learned to play little pieces on the harpsichord by ear, and not long afterward he began to compose pieces which his father wrote down for him. Soon he had learned to write them down for himself, and within a few years he had completely mastered the technic of composition. Meanwhile, both Wolfgang and his sister Marianne, who was five years older than himself, had become marvellous performers on the harpsichord, and when Wolfgang was only six years old their father took them to play at the courts of Munich and Vienna, where they were received with the greatest enthusiasm. In Vienna the Emperor called Wolfgang a "little magician," and made him play the harpsichord first with one finger only, and then with the keyboard covered, while the Empress, Maria Theresa, let him climb into her lap and kiss her as if she had been his mother.

Later Mozart made many concert tours, at

first with his sister and then alone, playing both the harpsichord and the pianoforte—which was just coming into fashion—in most of the cities and courts of Europe. He did not neglect his studies, however, in spite of the excitements and distractions of his career as a virtuoso, and he even found time to compose a great deal of music into the bargain. When he was fourteen years old he went to Rome, and there he performed a feat which proved that he had the most remarkable musical ear and memory that has ever been heard of. During Holy Week there was sung at the Sistine Chapel a *Miserere* by Allegri—a long and very complicated choral work, which was never permitted to be sung elsewhere. Mozart went to hear it, and when it was finished he wrote it down from memory, note for note, almost without a mistake.

Despite the brilliant beginning of his career and the universal recognition of his genius from the very start, although throughout his childhood and youth he was the pet of kings and queens, Mozart's life was not a very happy one. He was often ill, and being, like most artists, a poor business man, he found it very difficult to "make both ends meet." His concerts were often financial failures, and he was nearly always in debt.   Yet, in spite of all his troubles, his music is almost all of the gayest and happiest kind.

He did not write as many symphonies as Haydn—only forty-one—but some of them still rank as the greatest masterpieces of their kind, and in addition he composed an almost incredible number of other works, including many operas, cantatas, masses, concertos and other pieces.   His chief contribution to the orchestra itself was the introduction of the clarinet, which had been almost entirely neglected until he recognized its possibilities and began to compose for it.

Mozart died in 1791, eighteen years earlier than Haydn.

BEETHOVEN

After Haydn and Mozart came Beethoven, the greatest of all symphonists.   He was born in 1770, of Flemish parents, in the Prussian town of Bonn, where he lived until he was twenty-one.   Like Mozart, he received his first music lessons from his father, who was a member of the Court band of the Elector of Cologne, but he had not Mozart's phenomenal ear and aptness, and it is feared that, like Haydn, he had to be encouraged with numerous floggings.

Although he was recognized by his acquaintances as a boy of talent, he did not achieve in his youth the widespread fame which the young Mozart won so easily. When he was seventeen, however, he visited Vienna and played for Mozart, who is said to have remarked: "Pay attention to him; he will make a noise in the world some day." Five years later he returned to Vienna, to remain there to the end of his days. Up to this time he had accomplished nothing of particular importance. He was practically unknown outside of his native town of Bonn, and had composed very little music, none of which was of much importance. But now he set to work with tremendous energy, studying counterpoint and composition, first with Haydn, whom he did not like as a teacher, and then with Albrechtsberger, who did not like him as a pupil. The fact is that Beethoven was so headstrong that he could not get on with any teacher. He wanted to change all the rules of composition to suit himself, and refused to do as he was told. Such an attitude would have been fatal to any ordinary student; but Beethoven became a great composer in spite of it. He was a great genius.

Gradually he acquired a reputation in Vienna, both as a composer and as a pianist. He made many useful friends among the aristocracy, notwithstanding his eccentric manners and violent temper, and in spite of his open hatred of everything in the nature of class-distinction. For Beethoven was an ardent believer in the equality and brotherhood of man; he did not believe in kings and titles and the right of one man to oppress his fellows because he happened to be born with a crown on his head—or at least on his coat-of-arms. Nowadays he would be called a "radical"; in those days he was probably called a "queer fish," or whatever they *did* call people who had unusual ideas in the 18th Century.

The latter part of the 18th Century was, after all, a rather "radical" period. Both the American and French revolutions occurred during Beethoven's youth. He probably heard very little about the American revolution, which happened very far way, but the French one was nearer home, and Beethoven was very enthusiastic about it. He was particularly enthusiastic about a young general in the Republican Army, named Napoleon Bonaparte, in whom he thought he saw the ideal champion of liberty and equality, the deliverer of mankind from the oppression of crowned tyrants. To express his admiration of the young general he wrote a great symphony, called it the "Heroic Symphony," and dedicated it to Napoleon Bonaparte; but he had hardly finished the work when the young general put a crown upon his own head and declared himself Emperor of France. Beethoven was furious with disappointment and disgust. He tore the title page from his score and stamped upon it, exclaiming: "After all, he is nothing but an ordinary mortal! He will trample all the rights of men underfoot, and become a greater tyrant than any one!"

Such was the character of Beethoven—ardent, violent, eccentric. As he grew older his temper became more and more irritable, his manner more and more abrupt and harsh. But we cannot blame him for that when we realize the terrible fate which he saw slowly but surely closing in upon him. He was growing deaf. His hearing grew steadily worse, until finally it was lost altogether. Of his later works he never heard a single note, except in his own imagination. Could any one imagine a greater tragedy for a musician?

This tragedy, which embittered his life, also left its mark on his music. It made it sadder—

but it also made it greater, more profound. Whereas Haydn and Mozart composed simply for the joy of creating beautiful sounds, Beethoven wrote music to express his deepest thoughts and feelings—those thoughts and feelings which he could not express in words. He wrote but nine symphonies—but they are giants among symphonies. The fifth one, in C minor, is generally considered the greatest ever composed, and most of the others are nearly as fine. His other works include an opera, several overtures and concertos, a great Solemn Mass and a vast amount of chamber music (string quartets, etc.), music for the piano, and songs. What he did to increase the capacity of the orchestra is of the greatest importance. He introduced the trombone as a regular member of the brass section; he made independent solo instruments of all the brasses, which had previously been treated almost as if they were percussion instruments, being given only relatively unimportant notes to play here and there; he showed that the kettledrum was capable of something more than merely beating time, and wrote many effective solo passages for it. In short, he enlarged the scope and dramatic expressiveness of the entire orchestra and proved that orchestral music could be something more than a mere succession of pleasing sounds.

Beethoven died in 1827, at the age of fifty-six.

BERLIOZ

Hector Berlioz, born at Côte-St.-André, France, in 1803, was even more of a radical than Beethoven. He began by rebelling against his father's choice of a profession for him, continued to play the rebel in his studies, and throughout his life was constantly in revolt against somebody or something. His father, who was a country doctor, intended that his son should follow in his footsteps, and strictly forbade him to think of studying music. When, therefore, at the age of nineteen, he was sent to Paris to study medicine, he was without even the rudiments of a musical education; but he hated the very idea of being a doctor, and felt that he had it in him to become a composer. Accordingly, he defied his father, gave up the study of medicine, and devoted himself heart and soul to music.

He did not have an easy time of it. His family withdrew their financial support, and he was forced to earn a miserable living by singing in the chorus at some small theater. He quarreled with his instructors, scoffed at the rules of composition which they were trying to teach him, and got himself into innumerable rows and difficulties. Unlike Beethoven, he never succeeded in mastering the rules he scorned, and his works show the lack of proper training in the theory of music. In one respect only he triumphed over all his handicaps—orchestration. There his marvelous sense of tone-color and his practical knowledge of what each instrument could be made to do took the place of academic training, and made him one of the greatest masters of instrumentation. He did more than any other man to enlarge the dimensions and increase the effectiveness of the orchestra. He introduced the harp and English horn into the symphonic family, and discovered numberless new instrumental effects and combinations. He is said to have known the capacities of the various instruments better than did the players themselves.

Possessed of a vivid and soaring imagination and inexhaustible energy, he delighted in everything big, extravagant, and violent. He composed for orchestras of enormous proportions—one of his scores calls for 16 kettledrums—and in his famous treatise on orchestration he asserts that the ideal orchestra should contain 242 strings, 30 grand pianos, 30 harps, and wind and percussion instruments in proportion!

His compositions are intensely original and full of fire, though uneven in quality, owing to his deficient training. His symphonies, of which there are only four, are not really symphonies in the classic sense of the term, but symphonic poems with dramatic subjects. Indeed, practically all of his compositions are "programme music"—that is, music which endeavors to tells a story.

He died in Paris in 1869, after a life of tireless labor and incessant strife.

WAGNER

Another great musical rebel was Richard Wagner. He was born at Leipzig, in 1813. At first he intended to be a dramatic poet, but after hearing Beethoven's music to Goethe's "Egmont" he was so impressed with the dramatic possibilities of music that he determined to become a composer instead. He found it less easy than he had expected. The rules of harmony and counterpoint seemed uselessly complicated and unreasonably rigid to him, and, like Berlioz, he grew impatient with them. His progress was slow, partly because he was interested in so many things that his attention was constantly divided. Nevertheless, he did learn to compose, and in the end became the greatest writer of operas and one of the greatest masters of orchestration the world has yet seen.

His chief ambition was to bring about certain reforms in grand opera. He considered that the music should be more closely related to the plot and action of the drama—that it could, and should, be made to accompany the story enacted on the stage in such a way as to make its meaning clearer and more impressive. This he succeeded in accomplishing, in his great music dramas "The Ring of the Nibelung," "Tristan and Isolde," and "Parsifal." How he did it would take too long to explain here, as it would take too long to relate the many interesting events of his strenuous career—how he got himself involved in political troubles and was forced to leave Germany; how his operas met sometimes with success, sometimes with failure; and how he was finally befriended by the King of Bavaria, who helped him to realize all his artistic ideals. We shall have to content ourselves for the present with noting some of his contributions to the development of the orchestra.

In that respect he began where Berlioz left off. He, too, felt the need of more powerful and varied forces, and though he never made such extravant demands as Berlioz, he did considerably enlarge the orchestra. Instead of two flutes, two oboes, two clarinets, and two bassoons, he wrote for three of each, and he also added a bass clarinet and a double-bassoon to the wood-wind section. He adopted the tuba as a bass for his brass choir, and himself invented a whole set of brass instruments, something between horns and tubas, which were known as Wagner tubas. These instruments, however, have never come into general use. He also devised new and effective groupings of the various instruments, and discovered new possibilities in them. In short, he was hardly less bold as an innovator than Berlioz, and was much greater as a musician. He wrote only one symphony, and that in his early youth. It was lost for many years, and when found proved to be a work of very little importance; but his operas, or music dramas, are worthy to rank with the greatest symphonies, and they make even greater demands on the orchestra.

Wagner died at Venice in 1883, having had the satisfaction of seeing all his dreams come true during his lifetime.

The building of the orchestra did not end, of course, with Wagner's death. It has gone on ever since, and will doubtless go on as long as men continue to compose music. Among those who have recently added new stones to the structure we may mention Tschaikowsky, who was the first to recognize the value of the celesta; Rimsky-Korsakoff, who gave us new shades of tone color; Richard Strauss, who has startled us with strange combinations of sound and undreamed-of realistic effects; and Scriabine, who attempted to combine a "color organ" with the orchestra, in order that his music might be seen as well as heard. The result was not very encouraging, but someone else may yet succeed where Scriabine failed. Who can say what queer things may not be found in the orchestra a few years hence? The orchestra, unlike the cathedral will never be finished.

TYPICAL PROGRAMS OF CONCERTS FOR CHILDREN AND CONCERTS FOR YOUNG PEOPLE

Given by

THE NEW YORK SYMPHONY ORCHESTRA

WALTER DAMROSCH, CONDUCTOR

CONCERTS FOR CHILDREN

I

1. Suite from "Carmen"   .   .   .   *Bizet*
2. Andante from "Surprise" Symphony *Haydn*
3. Children's Corner   .   .   .   . *Debussy*
4. Turkish March   .   .   .   . *Mozart*

II

1. Overture, "Fingal's Cave"   *Mendelssohn*
2. Andante from Fifth Symphony *Beethoven*
3. March from "Lenore" Symphony .   . *Raff*
4. Dances from "Nutcracker" Suite.

Tschaikowsky

III

1. Overture to "Mignon" .   .   . *Thomas*
2. Andante from "Jupiter" Symphony *Mozart*
3. Polka-Mazurka, "The Dragon Fly"
   Johann Strauss
4. Triumphal March from "Aïda" . *Verdi*

IV

1. Overture to "William Tell" . *Rossini*
2. "Unfinished" Symphony (first movement)
   Schubert
3. a. Evensong .   .   .   . *Schumann*
      (Orchestrated by Saint-Saëns)
   b. Entrance of the Little Fauns from
      the Ballet "Cydalise" . . *Pierné*
4. March from "Tannhäuser" . . *Wagner*

V

1. Overture to "Der Freischütz" . *Weber*
2. Scherzo from Seventh Symphony *Beethoven*
3. Suite No. 1, from "Peer Gynt" . *Grieg*
4. Waltz, "Roses from the South"
   Johann Strauss

Concerts for Young People

I

1. Symphony in D (with the Hunting-horn Call) . . . . . . *Haydn*
2. Concerto in D, for Violin with Orchestra *Mozart*
   Soloist, Albert Spalding
3. a. St. Francis Preaching to the Birds *Liszt* (Orchestrated by Felix Mottl)
   b. Sounds of the Forest, from "Siegfried" *Wagner*

II

1. Symphony No. 2, in D . . *Beethoven*
2. Berceuse Héroïque . . . *Debussy*
3. Concerto in A, for Piano with Orchestra *Liszt*
   Soloist, Ossip Gabrilowitsch
4. French Military March, from "Algerian Scenes" . . . . . *Saint-Saëns*

III

Christmas Programme

1. Andante and Finale from Symphony No. 9 in C . . . . . *Schubert*

2. Medieval French and English Christmas
   Songs:
   a. Entre le Bœuf et l'Ane Gris (17th
      Century) . Arr. by *J. B. Weckerlin*
   b. Noël du Pays de Beaune (17th Cen-
      tury) Arr. by *Maurice Emmanuel*
   c. King Herod and the Cock (Worcester-
      shire) . . Arr. by *Cecil Sharp*
   d. As I Sat on a Sunny Bank (Worcest-
      ershire) . . Arr. by *Cecil Sharp*
      Soloist, Loraine Wyman
3. Pastorale from the Christmast Oratorio
   J. S. Bach

4. Folk Songs:
   a. La Belle Jalouse (Chanson Vosgienne)
      Arr. by *J. Minsmer*
   b. La Femme Embarrassée (Chanson
      Bretonne)
      Arr. by *Bourgault-Ducoudray*
   c. Lord Lovel } Old Ballads
   d. The Dumb Wife Cured } of the 18th Century
      Soloist, Loraine Wyman
5. Christmas Hymns
   (Sung by the Audience)
6. Children's March, "Over the Hills and
   Far Away" . . . *Percy Grainger*

IV

1. Symphony No. 4 ("Italian") *Mendelssohn*
2. Concerto in E-flat, for Two Pianos with
   Orchestra . . . . . *Mozart*
   Solists, Guy Maier and Lee Pattison
3. Overture to "Tannhäuser" . . *Wagner*

V

PART I

1. Prelude to Act III, "Lohengrin" *Wagner*
2. Second and Third Movements from Symphony No. 6 ("Pathétique") *Tschaikowsky.*

PART II

DANCE-PANTOMIMES PERFORMED BY MEMBERS OF
THE ADOLPH BOLM BALLET INTIME

1. Carnival . . . . . *Schumann*
   Ruth Page, Caird Leslie, Adolph Bolm
2. Humoresque . . . *Tschaikowsky*
   Margit Leeraas and Alexander Oumansky
3. Papillon . . . . . . *Grieg*
   Ruth Page
4. Pavane . . . . . . *Fauré*
   Margit Leeraas and Caird Leslie

5. Puss in Boots . . . *Tschaikowsky*
   Ruth Page and Frank Parker
6. Prelude, Op. 23, No. 5. . *Rachmaninoff*
   Margit Leeraas and Adolph Bolm
7. Dream of Love . . . . *Liszt*
   Ruth Page and Frank Parker
8. Spanish Dance . . . . *Albeniz*
   Adolph Bolm
9. The White Peacock . . . *Griffes*
   Margit Leeraas
10. Valse, Op. 34, No. 1 . . . *Chopin*
    Ruth Page
11. Assyrian Dance . . . . *Maloof*
    Adolph Bolm
12. Hopak . . . . *Moussorgsky*
    Margit Leeraas, Alexander Oumansky,
    and Ensemble